D0903984

Gertrude Stein

GERTRUDE STEIN

Avis Burnett

ILLUSTRATED WITH PHOTOGRAPHS

Atheneum 1972 New York

All photographs on jacket and in photograph section are from the Collection of Edward M. Burns, New York—Copyright by Mr. Burns and used with his permission—except the third picture in the photographic group—of writing table and art—which is reproduced from the original in the Yale University Library and used with permission.

Library of Congress catalog card number 72-75264
Published simultaneously in Canada by
McClelland & Stewart, Ltd.
Manufactured in the United States of America by
Halliday Lithograph Corporation
West Hanover, Massachusetts
First Edition

TO A. L. F.

"Every day is a renewal, every morning the daily miracle. This joy you feel is life."

Acknowledgments

The author gratefully acknowledges permission to use short excerpts from the following books:

Brinnin, John Malcolm, *The Third Rose: Gertrude Stein and Her World*, Boston, Little Brown, 1959. Reprinted 1968, Peter Smith, by special arrangement with Little Brown.

Fuller, Edmund, ed., *Journey Into the Self: Being the letters, papers and journals of Leo Stein*, New York, Crown, copyright 1950 by the estate of Leo D. Stein.

Picasso, Pablo, *Hunk of Skin*, trans. by Paul Blackburn, San Francisco, City Lights Books, 1968.

Rogers, W. G., *When This You See Remember Me: Gertrude Stein in Person*, Indianapolis, Bobbs-Merrill, 1948.

Stein, Gertrude, *The Autobiography of Alice B. Toklas*, New York, Alfred A. Knopf (Random House), 1960.

———, *Fernhurst, Q.E.D., and other early writings*, New York, Liverwright, 1971.

Van Vechten, Carl, ed., *Selected Writings of Gertrude Stein*, New York, Random House, 1962.

Gertrude Stein

one

"Once the problem is properly defined, the answer is relatively easy."

Gertrude Stein and her brother Leo were walking home from the city library where they had spent the morning reading their current favorite authors, Fielding and Scott. For two weeks Oakland, California, had huddled under drizzling rain and fog, but now the sun was out again. Feeling exuberant, Gertrude picked up a stick and ran it along a picket fence that bordered the sidewalk near their home.

"Act your age, Gertrude!" Leo said in a low voice, casting sidelong glances at people passing by. "Seventeen-year-old girls don't play sticks on fences. That's for eight-year-old boys."

"You're a stuffed shirt, Leo, and a grumpy one at that."

"I don't know why you're so carefree. You ought to be sober enough this afternoon. Being ordered into Father's study is no laughing matter. What did you do this time?" Leo turned into the front gate of their home.

Gertrude shrugged as she closed the gate behind them. "With Father, who knows? You'd think this was New England, 1600, not California, 1891."

"Gertrude!" their father called sharply from his study window. "Come in at once. I've been waiting for you."

"Aren't you the lucky one," Leo muttered.

Inside the dark masculine study, Gertrude watched her father defiantly. Staccato thoughts edged with annoyance flitted through her mind. Daniel Stein. Successful businessman. Unsympathetic father. She felt no love for him, and she was sure he felt none for her. Hadn't he often told her that she was a disappointment to him?

Her father leaned back in his leather chair and twirled a pencil between his fingers. As Gertrude watched him, she realized again how much she missed her mother. Even though her mother had been dead for three years, Gertrude could vividly remember her loving voice, the proud way she carried her head, her attention to manners, and her fiery temper.

Suddenly Daniel tipped his chair forward and clasped his hands on the desk in front of him. "You are a great disappointment to me, Gertrude," he began in a low controlled voice. "In spite of all the advantages I have given you, you are rebellious and seem to be at cross-purposes with conventional life. Why this is so remains a mystery."

Gertrude had heard this speech before, although it was usually delivered with more force and preceded by invectives and threats. She watched a fly dart in and out of the afternoon shadows that were spreading across the room. For what seemed an unbearably long time, she waited for Daniel to continue, but the only sound in the room was the noisy buzzing of the fly.

Finally Gertrude stole a look at her father. She followed his gaze to the trees outside the window that faced Tenth Street. He apparently was looking at nothing. Lord, *why* didn't he get on with it . . .

"Sometimes, Gertrude," Daniel said, turning from the window with a sigh, "I wish you were still five years old and we were living in Vienna and Paris again. You were affectionate then, alert, lovable, wanting to please—all you children were. Those were happy days."

Gertrude stared at her father. Daniel Stein, sentimental? She could scarcely believe her ears. She was used to his exploding in outbursts of temper, used to his being on edge with the rest of the family. But she was not used to hearing him reminisce.

Daniel got to his feet and began slowly pacing back and forth behind his desk. "Do you know what the neighbors are saying about you, Gertrude?" he asked at last.

"No, sir, I don't."

"They are calling you a streetwalker!" Daniel stopped pacing and let the words sink in.

Gertrude eyed her father evenly.

"A *streetwalker*," Daniel said again, almost shouting this time and leaning far across his desk. "And do you know why?"

"No, sir."

"Because you leave the house late at night, after I'm asleep, and don't return until three or four in the morning. I want an explanation!"

"Leo and I read in the evening," Gertrude answered boldly. "After sitting so long I like to stretch my legs. So I go for a walk."

"Until three or four in the morning?"

"Sometimes I walk until the sun comes up."

"My God," Daniel moaned, dropping heavily into his chair. "How could I have sired such a litter? Five children, and Michael is the only one with any common sense. At least Simon and Bertha have an excuse. Neither of them was bright to begin with. But you and Leo have brains sticking out of your ears. What's *your* excuse?"

Gertrude looked at the floor.

"Michael is the only comfort I have," Daniel continued, ignoring Gertrude's silence. "There's some peace in knowing that when I die he can handle my affairs. Thank God he's home from Johns Hopkins. He'll make sure Simon and Bertha have satisfactory futures . . . But you and Leo!" Daniel fixed Gertrude with a steady gaze. "You're so scatter-brained that without me you are likely to ruin not only your own lives but other people's as well."

"Why are you talking this way?" Gertrude burst out. "You sound as if you expect to die tomorrow."

"Maybe I do," Daniel thundered back. "And if I should, be certain that you will have to make many decisions, not against me, as you have done so often in the past, but for yourself. When this happens, remember . . ."

Gertrude filled in the words in her mind as her father spoke them, ". . . *the key to a successful life is proper decision making*." Remember! How could she forget? She had heard this advice at least once every day of her life.

". . . when making a decision," Daniel's voice broke into Gertrude's thoughts, "*first carefully define the problem.* Once the problem is properly defined, the answer is relatively easy. Are you listening to me, Gertrude?"

"I'm listening."

"But did you hear?"

"I heard."

"Very well, you may go now."

Just before sunup the next morning, Gertrude was awakened by a California thrasher singing a harsh *wheek, wheek*, from the tree outside her window. "Bothersome bird," she muttered to herself. She didn't like to wake up so early, for it was her habit either to walk or read at night and sleep during the morning. Although her father was strict about his children's moral principles, he paid little attention to their sleeping or eating habits.

When Amelia Stein was alive, the family had lived according to a strict schedule with regular hours for everything. The household ran smoothly under Amelia's superb management. But since her death, there had been no one to maintain order. As the oldest daughter, Bertha had tried to cook for a while. However, Bertha was neither clever nor ambitious, and she soon declared the work too much for her and gave up. Gertrude couldn't remember the last time the whole family had eaten a meal together.

Gertrude sat up in bed. Now that the bird had awakened her, she couldn't get to sleep again. Her mind went back to the previous afternoon. What did her father's strange behavior mean?

On the other side of the room, Bertha moved restlessly in her bed. Gertrude watched her sister's bulky form turn first one way and then another. Bertha's fatter than I, she thought. This idea pleased and amused her.

Both Gertrude and Bertha loved to eat, and both were overweight. But Bertha worried about her size; she was afraid no one would want to marry her. Gertrude didn't worry about getting married, for Leo was the only man in her life. Besides, eating was one of the things she enjoyed most. She liked nothing better than to spend an afternoon or evening with a book and a bowl of fruit and nuts, relishing and devouring them all.

Suddenly the morning quiet was interrupted by yelling and pounding in the hallway. "What's that noise?" Bertha mumbled, sitting up in bed, her hair disheveled and her eyelids heavy with sleep.

Gertrude had already pulled on her robe and flung open the bedroom door. At the end of the hall she could see Leo pounding on the door of their father's room. Gertrude hurried toward him. "Why are you making such a racket?"

"I can't wake Father. Last night he asked me to get him up at five, and here it is after six."

"Do you have a key?"

"A key to *his* room? You know he wouldn't allow any of us to have one. I've tried picking the lock, but the spring won't budge." Leo started down the stairs, two at a time.

"Where are you going?"

"To get a ladder from the storeroom," Leo yelled over his shoulder. "I'm going to crawl across the roof to his window."

Gertrude followed him down the stairs. Together they dragged the heavy ladder from the storeroom to the side of the house.

"Why do you think he doesn't answer?" Gertrude asked as she helped Leo adjust the ladder against the eaves.

"I don't know. Hold it steady now, I don't want to break my neck."

Leo climbed the ladder and eased himself onto the roof. Carefully he inched along it until he reached his father's window. Lifting the sash, he disappeared inside.

Gertrude waited for what seemed like hours. Cautiously

she climbed a few rungs of the ladder. Just then she saw Leo backing out of their father's window. She climbed down and steadied the ladder. "Did you get him up?" she called.

"No, I couldn't."

"Why?"

Leo made his way down the ladder, stumbling on the last rung. Then he turned around and looked at her. "Because, Gertrude," he said slowly, "Father is dead."

"Dead!"

Leo nodded.

"Are you sure?" Gertrude whispered.

"Oh he's dead all right," Leo replied, pulling the ladder off the eaves. "He isn't breathing, no heartbeat, and he's stiff as a board. I tried to unlock the door, but it's stuck. Why in thunder do you suppose he locked the door?"

Gertrude felt numb. "Maybe he knew he was going to die," she offered feebly.

"Huh!" Leo snorted. "Only saints know that, and he was no saint. All he thought about was making money and keeping our lives in turmoil. Anyway, sure as the devil, he's dead." Adjusting one end of the ladder on his shoulder, Leo started toward the house. Dazed, Gertrude picked up the other end and followed.

"What do you do when someone dies?" Leo asked. "Do you call a doctor?"

Gertrude didn't answer.

"Well, Michael will know," Leo said, opening the door to the storeroom. "We'd better go wake him."

two

"I want to be somebody!"

From her train seat, Gertrude watched the Kansas plains roll by, flat, empty, and endless. Leo sat next to her reading a book. Shifting uncomfortably in his seat, he tried to make more room for his long legs. His reddish hair drooped over his glasses, giving his long thin face a studious look. In the seat behind them Bertha was embroidering a pillow slip.

Gertrude couldn't read; she had too many things to think about. So much had happened since her father's death more than a year before. First there had been the elaborate funeral, attended by some of the most prominent businessmen in San Francisco. Then a managerial position had been offered to Michael by the railroad magnate, Collis P. Huntington. Finally a letter had come from Uncle Eph and Aunt Fanny Bachrach asking Gertrude, Leo, and Bertha to stay with them in Baltimore.

"Much as I'd miss you," Michael had said after reading

the letter aloud, "I think you should go." Gertrude had cringed, even though she knew living with Uncle Eph and Aunt Fanny would be exciting. Uncle Eph was a sculptor, firmly established in Baltimore's best social and intellectual circles. But Baltimore seemed so far away! Of course it would be better for Michael if he were relieved of some of the family responsibilities. Gertrude knew well enough that acting as personal and financial guardian had been difficult for him.

After Daniel Stein's death, the burden of the whole family had fallen on Michael. At first he had seemed stunned. But within weeks he had collected his wits and had so brilliantly maneuvered his father's railroad investments that he could assure each of his brothers and sisters a small but adequate allowance for the rest of their lives.

For Michael's sake then, Gertrude and Bertha were going to Baltimore. Leo was traveling with them, but he didn't plan to stay with Uncle Eph and Aunt Fanny very long. Soon he would be enrolling at Harvard. Simon would stay in Oakland and work as a cable car gripman.

When the three Steins alighted from the train in Baltimore and Gertrude felt the warmth of Aunt Fanny's embrace and saw the twinkle in Uncle Eph's eye, all her reservations about coming East vanished. Baltimore had charm, and Uncle Eph and Aunt Fanny seemed like family. Here she and Leo and Bertha could feel that they truly belonged, for their mother's parents also lived in Baltimore, and their Uncle Solomon Stein and Aunt Pauline lived nearby in New York City.

Aunt Fanny ran a meticulously managed household. Breakfast was at seven, lunch at twelve, tea at four, and dinner at seven-thirty. Everyone would please be on time! And everyone was. The undisciplined Steins quickly learned to be orderly and well-mannered. None of them objected, for they all liked and wanted to please Aunt Fanny.

Gertrude's days were full of companionship and activity. She was never bored, as she had sometimes been in Oakland, nor did she suffer from the periods of dark depression that had often beset her. Aunt Fanny encouraged her to go out with other young people, and soon she was part of a fashionable and witty group who attended the theater and opera regularly.

Uncle Solomon and Aunt Pauline sent warm greetings and expressed a desire to see them all soon. But months passed, and the Solomon Steins still did not arrive. Gertrude inquired one day how long they must wait for "soon." Uncle Eph explained that it was rare indeed for Solomon to be away from his business, for he was very successful and very rich and he loved working hard to stay that way.

"Don't get in a tither, Gertrude," Uncle Eph advised. "We may not see them until next year and maybe not even then." But Uncle Eph was wrong. In a few days Aunt Fanny received word that Uncle Solomon and Aunt Pauline were coming to spend the weekend.

Gertrude was curious to meet her aunt and uncle, for a disagreement between them and her parents had played a major role in her life. Until Gertrude was six months old, Daniel and Solomon Stein had both lived in Baltimore with their families and owned a mercantile business together. But because of an argument between Amelia and Pauline, the partnership had dissolved and Daniel had taken his family abroad. Gertrude knew nothing about the misunderstanding, except that her mother never did forgive and forget. Uttering the name Pauline in Amelia's presence provoked dark looks and a dangerous silence.

Much to Gertrude's surprise, when Uncle Solomon and Aunt Pauline arrived for the weekend, she liked them at once. Aunt Pauline was loving and full of robust good spirits; Uncle Solomon had a firm handshake and a hearty laugh.

After a convivial family dinner, Gertrude and Leo went with Uncle Solomon to the front porch for some after-dinner talk. The conversation inevitably turned to Daniel. As usual, talk about their father made Leo edgy.

"Your father was a smart man," Uncle Solomon said, settling back in the porch swing with a freshly lighted cigar. "Smart, but cantankerous. He used to drive away more customers than I could bring in when we were in business together. But how he could make money! Think of it. Your whole family lived in Europe for five years on what your father earned in Baltimore. And in style, too: special tutoring, art classes, musical entertainment. When your father moved you to California from Paris, he still had enough money to invest in railroads and land and buy that fancy Stratton Place where you lived in Oakland."

"Oh Father could make money, all right," Leo said dryly.

"There's nothing wrong with making money," Uncle Solomon replied shortly. "Where would you be if your father hadn't invested wisely? You wouldn't be going to Harvard, I can tell you. Nor gadding about all day looking at pictures in art galleries."

Leo had been sitting on the porch steps beside Gertrude. Now he stood up. "I would like to have had less money and more love," he said.

"Bah! What do you think love is for a man anyway, if it isn't providing for his family?"

"It isn't being a tyrant as Father was!" Leo shot back. Leo's silhouette contrasted sharply with the light that arched across the porch from the parlor. Gertrude could see that he was trembling.

"Tyrant!" Uncle Solomon snorted. "What do you know about tyrants at your age?"

"I lived with one," Leo muttered. Turning abruptly, he went inside the house. The screen door slammed behind him.

Gertrude watched the end of Uncle Solomon's cigar get red and then die down. Finally he said, "Your brother has a lot to learn, Gertrude. I hope you're not as emotional as he is."

"Leo's obsessed with the idea that Father ruined his childhood," Gertrude replied. "He spends hours brooding over the past. For me that's a waste of time—I want to think of the future. I want to be somebody! What would you say if I told you I wanted to enroll at the Harvard Annex for Women?"

"I'd say that for most girls it would be damn foolish. But if you want to make something of yourself, that's a good place to start."

That night Gertrude wrote a letter:

> Dear Sir:
>
> This letter is a request for admittance to the Harvard Annex for Women. I am not familiar with your requirements, but I feel confident that I could pass whatever examinations are necessary for matriculation, for I have an extraordinary learning capacity. My knowledge of history and

English literature is above average and I read German and French excellently. I am nineteen years old.

Yours truly,
Gertrude Stein

Before long Gertrude received a reply informing her that Harvard would be glad to consider her application after she had satisfactorily completed a series of tests. Gertrude went to Cambridge, took the tests, and was soon notified that she had passed.

"They admitted you!" Leo exclaimed when he heard the news. "There must be some mistake. Harvard requires a proficient reading ability in Latin. You don't know any Latin; you couldn't have passed the entrance examination."

"There's no mistake," Gertrude said confidently. "They were going to test me in Latin, but I told them they would be wasting their time since I didn't know a word of it."

"And still they admitted you?"

"Yes."

Leo looked at his sister in amazement. "Ever since you were small," he said, "you've been able to manipulate people and circumstances. And you always come out ahead. I don't know how you do it."

"Expect the best and you get it," Gertrude replied airily. "I think I will succeed, and so I do. It's as simple as that."

three

"Create! Let go! Your mind will come back soon enough to the mundane world."

When Gertrude arrived at the boarding house where she was to stay while attending school, her trunks contained enough books, mostly English classics, to fill one wall of her room from floor to ceiling. This left little space in her baggage for clothes, which was the way she liked it—many books and few clothes.

Unlike most girls, she thought clothes should be purely functional. Aunt Fanny thought differently. When she saw Gertrude's colorless, shapeless dresses being packed, she began pulling them out of the trunks. "You can't wear these rags," she cried. "Tomorrow we are going shopping for a fashionable wardrobe. Why, you don't even have a corset!"

But Gertrude wouldn't be swayed. "I want to be comfortable," she said firmly, repacking her clothes. "I do not want to be fashionable, nor do I want to be corseted!"

Gertrude made friends easily at Cambridge and was soon very popular. She adapted quickly to living with other young people. Both men and women enjoyed her company. Women liked her daring and unconventional ways, and men liked her rollicking sense of humor and her clever and incisive mind.

Thriving under the sharp stimulation of new ideas that sparkled everywhere on the Harvard campus, Gertrude plunged into her studies. She took a course in philosophy under George Santayana, a course in metaphysics under Josiah Royce, and a course in psychology under Hugo Munsterberg. The young Munsterberg, who had just recently come from Berlin, was so impressed with her abilities that he used her as a model for the ideal American scholar in a publication he sent to Europe.

Since psychology was a challenging new science and one that provoked lively discussions, Gertrude was drawn to it. She read avidly and performed brilliantly in class. Professor Munsterberg was delighted with her progress and encouraged her in every way he could. "I recommended to Professor William James that you be admitted into his graduate seminar," he told her one day. "After looking over your records, Professor James was glad to make an opening for you, even though you are still an undergraduate."

Gertrude was elated over this unusual opportunity and looked forward to the first lecture. Leo had studied under William James and had been completely devoted to him. "My own thinking goes so absolutely on all fours with his," Leo had said.

Professor James' seminar was everything Gertrude expected and more. "A metaphysician of the highest degree," she noted after the first lecture. "A man with vigorous originality, dignity, courage, sympathy. . ." She couldn't find enough superlatives to describe him.

"Ideas, ideas!" William James told the class, his beard bobbing up and down exuberantly. "For every man who has one, you may find a hundred who are willing to drudge patiently at some unimportant experiment."

Gertrude had previously prided herself on being observant and willing to seek out new experiences, but now, under the influence of Professor James' alert mind, she realized that she had used only a small portion of her potential. Certainly she had never known the excitement of using her mind as a tool for directing flights through imagination and time.

She embarked upon project after project. Fascinated by the personalities of her fellow students, she studied their characters as reflected in speech patterns and categorized them into two groups: independent-dependent, and dependent-independent. Then she studied the problem of perceiving reality in time, concluding that the answer was to capture the ongoing ever-present moment.

Professor James thought her work good, even excellent. "Create!" he urged her. "Let your stream of consciousness flow, wandering where it will, so your mind can fly and perch as a bird does. Let go! Your mind will come back soon enough to the drudgery of the mundane world. You only have to call it." Stimulated, hardly aware that she was working long hours, Gertrude became a superior student.

The culmination of Gertrude's work in psychology was a project handled jointly with her seminar partner, Leon Solomons. Together they experimented with memory, attention, color saturation, and automatic writing. Although they didn't always agree, they were critical and honest in their reaction, and their efforts resulted in a published report in the *Psychological Review* for September, 1896, called *Normal Motor Automatism.*

As Gertrude's days at the Harvard Annex, now called Radcliffe, proceeded steadily toward graduation, a major obstacle stood in her path—she had never passed the Latin requirement for entrance and thus could not be awarded a degree. When school officials reminded her of this, she began carrying a Latin grammar book under her arm, but she didn't study even though the test was imminent.

"How can I study?" Gertrude reasoned with herself. Leo had quit working toward his degree in history and was urging her to spend the summer traveling with him in Europe. She couldn't concentrate on Latin when Europe was beckoning. Although a friend tried to tutor her, Gertrude's heart wasn't in it. She failed the examination.

To escape the unpleasant truth that through delinquency she had postponed her graduation, Gertrude further jeopardized her academic reputation by failing to prepare for that year's final examinations. Instead of studying, she indulged in her current passion, opera, sometimes going twice in one day.

Inevitably, examination day arrived. Although Gertrude was totally unprepared, she wanted to make a good showing. Nervous and apprehensive, she sat down for the first test. Quickly she read through the questions and then sank back in her chair with relief. *She knew the answers.* Her spirits rose. Maybe she would make high marks after all.

One after another she completed the tests, finding none of them as difficult as she had anticipated. At last only one test remained, Professor James'. Gertrude picked up the examination sheet with confidence, but as she read the questions, her heart sank. She couldn't hope to answer them. There was only one thing to do. In her scrawling script she wrote across the top of the test sheet:

Dear Professor James,
I am so sorry but really
I do not feel like an
examination paper today.

Under the curious stares of her classmates, Gertrude gathered up her books and left. She walked straight to her room, changed into fresh clothes, and arrived at the opera in time for the evening performance.

The next day she received a note from Professor James:

Dear Miss Stein,
I understand perfectly how you feel.
I often feel like that myself.

On the bottom of the note was her mark for the course, the highest he gave.

Gertrude breathed a sigh of relief. She was certain she had done well on her other exams. With this mark from Professor James, she could still graduate *magna cum laude* if she passed the Latin requirement. But for the present she wouldn't worry about it. Time enough next fall to study Latin, after she had tasted life abroad with Leo.

four

"I did what I had to do to keep from being bored, and that was worth all the degrees in the world."

With an untroubled conscience, Gertrude sailed for Europe, where Leo was waiting. The two of them spent a happy and relaxing summer. Leo had carefully planned the agenda, which included touring the low countries, a steamer trip up the Rhine, and a lengthy stay in Paris.

During their travels they treated themselves to culinary and aesthetic whims as fancy struck, disrupting their schedule to select just the right melon or to attend just the right art show. Some nights they lingered over dinner until dawn, debating some principle of art or philosophy. Their affection for each other deepened, and Gertrude realized more than ever how much she preferred Leo's companionship to that of all other people she knew.

At summer's end they both returned to America. Leo didn't go back to Harvard, for history no longer interested him. Instead he enrolled at Johns Hopkins, where he began to study biology. Gertrude, in the meantime, studied for and passed her Latin test at Radcliffe.

After graduating *magna cum laude* with the class of 1898, Gertrude also enrolled at Johns Hopkins where, as Professor James urged, she hoped to earn a degree in medicine. On impulse, she and Leo took a house together within easy walking distance of the medical school. The neighborhood was not fashionable and the house was too large, but Leo made the interior interesting by hanging Japanese prints. They hired a housekeeper and settled into a pattern of attending classes, studying, and entertaining friends on the weekends.

At first their relatives viewed this enterprise with outspoken skepticism. Aunt Fanny disapproved of the neighborhood; Uncle Eph doubted that they could manage their finances. But these attitudes changed as the months wore on and Gertrude and Leo demonstrated sound maturity in affairs of routine living.

Non-routine matters, however, brought out the fun-loving and rebellious sides of their characters. Freshly influenced by European styles in dress and thought, they startled friends by wearing woolen socks with sandals and dark loose-fitting clothes, and by their intense preoccupation with anything intellectual.

Each Saturday night Leo leaned against his favorite bookcase and directed discussions that sometimes lasted five or six hours. To entertain their guests and to enliven Leo's rather pedantic discourses, Gertrude told amusing anecdotes punctuated by great peals of her warm deep laughter.

Gertrude became more and more fond of their way of life and supposed that Leo did, too. She didn't notice how restless and irritable he was becoming until one morning he stormed into the kitchen while she was eating breakfast. "Johns Hopkins is an inane institution!" he exploded. "Instead of hiring clever professors, they contract with uninspired dullards. And the senseless detail these simpletons love to enforce! I'm kept so busy with meaningless assignments there isn't time left for reading anything worthwhile. Formal classroom work is tommyrot. I'm through with it!" Within a week Leo had packed and was off to Europe where, as he told Gertrude, he could afford to be his own master.

With Leo gone, Gertrude was faced with what she considered a staggering responsibility—running the household by herself. How could she manage a housekeeper, make decisions on the trifling annoyances that accompanied the running of a household, and keep her mind on classwork? At first she thought she would have to give up the house. But after considering the freedom she enjoyed, her mind was quickly swayed in favor of staying.

To help defray expenses, she invited Emma Lootz—a fellow student, studying to be an orthopedic surgeon—to move in with her. Emma was dependable and even-tempered and she discreetly overlooked Gertrude's Bohemian living habits.

Only once did she scold Gertrude, and then very gently. On that occasion Emma had spent an unusually long day at the university and was looking forward to a simple dinner and a quiet evening. To her dismay and alarm, when she opened the front door she was greeted by swaying chandeliers and the sound of bumps and loud groans coming from Gertrude's bedroom. Racing up the stairs, she threw open the door in time to hear Gertrude yell, "Give me one in the jaw. Now, give me one in the stomach!"

"What in heaven's name are you doing?" Emma demanded, looking in astonishment from Gertrude to a very muscular young man.

"We're boxing," Gertrude retorted, hardly looking up. "Hit me harder," she yelled at the young man, "you're not hitting hard enough. I want a *sweat* out of this."

Obligingly, Gertrude's partner threw well-aimed and forceful punches, which she deftly blocked. Emma backed quietly out of the room.

That night at dinner Emma confronted Gertrude. "I don't think you should be alone with a man in the house. It shows poor taste, even if you are boxing. If you *must* box, please wait until I'm home so the neighbors won't talk."

Gertrude picked up her knife and fork and cut into one of the two large steaks on her plate. "No, I must box, and I can arrange for my partner to come only at certain times. If you aren't home, I must box anyway."

"Why must you?"

"Because my blood is weak, and I think boxing will make it strong."

"Oh," Emma said.

While Gertrude was a student at Johns Hopkins, she spent most of her summers in Europe with Leo. But one summer she went to San Francisco to be introduced to Michael's fiancée, Sarah Samuels. Michael met Gertrude at the station. "I want you to like Sarah," he told her on the way home. "And I hope you will send a good report to Leo. Sarah is an intelligent and refined young woman. You should be proud to have her as part of the family."

"Sarah and I will get along," Gertrude said tartly, "if

she reads Browning well. I have already determined that that is to be the criterion."

That night the three of them had dinner together. Much to Michael's relief, when Gertrude handed Sarah a copy of Browning and asked her to read, she accepted graciously and read superbly.

As the summer wore on, the two young women grew very fond of each other. Sarah assumed the role of older sister and tried hard to temper Gertrude's outspoken ways. However, she had little success.

"Please, Gertrude," she pleaded before the guests arrived for one of Sarah's special afternoon teas, "be refined in your remarks. Ladies from some of San Francisco's best families will be here."

"I'll try," Gertrude promised.

Early in the afternoon, though, talk turned to the suffragette movement, which Gertrude couldn't bear to hear discussed. She listened quietly for a while and then lost patience. "The trouble with most suffragettes," she said in a loud voice, "is the same thing that's wrong with girls from Smith."

"What's that, dear?" Sarah inquired politely.

"Raw virginity!" Gertrude announced.

Teacups rattled noisily around the room. "Gertrude!" Sarah gasped.

Gertrude looked at her innocently. "Do you think there's more than *that* wrong with them?" she asked.

After spending a carefree summer in San Francisco, Gertrude reluctantly returned to Johns Hopkins. Influenced by Leo's disenchantment with schoolwork, Gertrude's interest, too, began to dim. She alienated professors and students alike by her moodiness and irresponsibility toward assignments and laboratory work. Such men as Halstead and Barker appreciated her mind and therefore tolerated her attitude, but some of the lesser staff members quickly took offense. When friends warned her of the inevitable consequences of what she was doing, she shrugged off their well-meaning advice and countered with, "I'm bored—you don't understand what it is to be bored."

Only one course sparked an interest in her, a class in obstetrics where she was required to midwife in the Negro section of the city. She disliked the professor in charge, but she looked forward to the assignments, for she was fascinated by the Negro people.

Sometimes as she worked, surrounded by dark glistening bodies, she was caught up in their rhythm. She could see it crest in the screaming and sobbing of a young Negro mother. She could feel it in the brown supple hands of a Negro doctor as he comforted and delivered. She could hear it in the low crooning of a Negro midwife as she held a new-born baby and wiped the sweat from the mother's face.

One night after a delivery, the rhythm was so strong in Gertrude that she could hardly think of anything else. "Create!" she could hear Professor James say, "Create!" But how? Suddenly she knew. She would use the rhythm as a kind of metronome, fashioning sentences around its variations.

Hurrying home, she went straight to her desk. Stacks of overdue classwork lay piled before her, but she ignored them and began to write. She continued through the night until the sun began to lighten the eastern sky. Finally she put her pen down and listened to the birds call to each other. Sometime during the night a vague uneasiness that had plagued her for as long as she could remember had been quieted. Had it been stilled through feeling? Through writing? She wasn't sure. . .

As graduation time drew near, Gertrude's marks were dangerously low. One of her professors, Dr. Williams, took her aside after class. "Miss Stein, your work does not merit passing, but to be fair, I have decided to question you orally."

Gertrude readily agreed, and the session began. However, each time Dr. Williams asked a question, Gertrude looked at him blankly. "Miss Stein," Professor Williams said, tapping his fingers on his desk, "I have asked you question after question which you refused to answer. Will you please tell me why?"

"Because, sir, I don't know the answers."

"Preposterous! You have one of the best minds in this medical school, and you try to make a fool of me by saying that you don't know the answers. Miss Stein, your attitude is unbearable!"

When the final marks were sent out, Gertrude received a "5" in Dr. William's class, a grade too low for passing.

News of her failure quickly spread throughout the school. Her friends begged her to consult with Dr. Williams and plead for another chance. "Absolutely not!" Gertrude replied, her shoulders thrown back and her hands stuck deep in the pockets of her brown corduroy dress. "I didn't *earn* passing marks. But I did what I had to do to keep from being bored, and that was worth all the degrees in the world." Having made this announcement to her friends, Gertrude went for a walk.

A message from Dr. Williams was tacked to her bedroom door when Gertrude returned home. "Please come to my office immediately," it read. Reluctantly she went.

"Failing was no doubt a great shock to you, Miss Stein," Dr. Williams began. "Of course it doesn't have to mean the end of your academic career. You can still take a degree by enrolling in a summer course."

"I wouldn't think of it," Gertrude quickly replied. "You have no idea how grateful I am to you. I have so much inertia and so little initiative that very possibly if you had not kept me from taking my degree, I would have continued in pathological psychology. And really, you can't imagine how I dislike it."

Dr. Williams looked thoughtful. Then he said quietly, "Very well, Miss Stein, you are dismissed."

In spite of Gertrude's show of bravado, she didn't feel good about failing her medical degree. She was twenty-six, with a degree from Radcliffe and almost another from Johns Hopkins behind her. Yet she wasn't prepared to do anything. "It's 1900," she consoled herself. "The new century and I will start together."

"You should have swallowed your pride and accepted Dr. Williams' offer," Emma scolded when Gertrude told her about the summer school suggestion.

"Not on your life!" Gertrude replied. "That would be making education political."

"What makes you think education isn't political, especially with women? Now that we have gained some privileges though, we should take our degrees, even if we have to use female ingenuity. I wore my best hat with roses on it when I was examined for my degree."

"Then I will never get one," Gertrude laughed. "Not even a rose in my hat would make me look feminine."

"But what are you going to do?" Emma pressed.

"I'm going to Europe."

"Oh Gertrude," Emma admonished, "that's no solution, to run away from the problem. What will you do after you get there?"

"Do as I please and thank my lucky stars that I've escaped the depressing tentacles of psychology and medicine."

five

"I like to clear my head the hard way, by baking *out the mold and cobwebs."*

During the boat trip to Europe, Gertrude had time to consider her future and the consequences of her academic failure. Her thoughts turned first to Michael and Leo. Michael had written to say how disappointed he was that she had spoiled an otherwise brilliant scholastic record. Leo, when he heard rumors that she might not graduate, had written a long letter encouraging her to finish, since she was apparently the only one in the family who might do so. "Well, I suppose you will," he ended, "especially as there's nothing else to be done. If you had my very superior talents for loafing, it might do, but you haven't, so it won't."

Laziness, though, was not the reason Gertrude had become negligent about classwork. Rather it was that psychology and medicine had begun to bore her. Now, with an advanced degree safely out of the picture, she could acknowledge that what she really wanted was to devote her life to scholarly reading and writing. By doing this she hoped to realize a long-held dream: *she wished to be an historically important person.*

Gertrude met Leo in Italy early in the summer. As usual, they wanted to see and do everything. For a while they lived in Perugia in the Umbrian valley, then, captivated by the charms of Assisi, they moved there. Using Assisi as a center, they took long hikes through the countryside, always eager for an unusual view or for a chance to see a new art show.

In August they toured London. Leo liked it so well that he persuaded Gertrude they should take a flat at 20 Bloomsbury Square. They had hardly settled in their new living quarters when a note came from Bernard Berenson and his wife asking Leo and Gertrude to spend a weekend at their home in Haslemere.

Leo had met the well-known critic and connoisseur of Italian Renaissance art while Gertrude was attending Johns Hopkins. He had written at the time: "I met Bernard Berenson, and am now under his spell—absolutely! I haven't been so impressed with a mind since taking classes under Wm. James. As with Wm. James, B.B.'s mind and mine click precisely together. He likes to analyze me and says my trouble is that I am forever inventing the umbrella." Gertrude was curious to meet this man who so favorably compared with William James and who had so adroitly labeled Leo.

Gertrude and Leo arrived at Haslemere dressed in their usual monk-like gowns and sandals. Persons more concerned with appearance would have felt acutely out of place, for Mr. and Mrs. Berenson entertained with elegance, and their manner of living was much in keeping with the superb paintings that hung everywhere in their home. But neither Gertrude nor Leo cared a whit about appropriate dress. They were primarily interested in the minds of their acquaintances.

The weekend was especially gratifying to Leo since among the guests were the novelist and playwright Israel Zangwill and a brilliant young mathematician, Bertrand Russell. Surrounded by these people, Leo felt that he had definitely come into his own. Here were persons worthy of his time.

Gertrude was less impressed. She and Bertrand Russell argued vehemently over the American character. He stated that Americans were closed-minded to new political ideas on the flimsiest of excuses—patriotism. She stated that his logic was unforgivably bad—patriotism was not an excuse, it was an ideal.

Although not swayed by the eminence of the Berensons' guests, Gertrude was so charmed by the gentle contours and rich autumnal colors of the English countryside that she quickly fell in with Leo's notion of renting a cottage nearby. During their stay at "Greenhill" cottage, Leo spent most evenings with the Berensons. Gertrude gladly used this time for reading.

In October they returned to London and their flat at Bloomsbury Square. Leo was aflame with becoming a critic and artist; and Gertrude, feeling that he was justified in his ambitions, encouraged him by listening as he developed one principle of aesthetics after another.

Gertrude spent her free time in the Reading Room of the British Museum, poring over the plays of Robert Greene and the novels of Trollope. As a young girl reading Shakespeare and the Bible, she had seldom opened a book without a note pad and pencil at hand. Now, behind the walls of the British Museum, she resumed this habit and was happy to discover that she had a sense for the palpability of words. She liked to "handle" them at the end of her pen or put them in her mouth and savor their taste.

Leisure time for reading and easy accessibility to good books were much to Gertrude's liking, but the dreariness of London in the winter sometimes seemed more than she could bear. Some days her mood dropped so low that she felt threatened by the depressions she had suffered in her youth. She feared these "dark times" above all else, for at their worst they were climaxed by a feeling of desolation, of nothingness. In this state she could not identify herself or her relationship to anything around her.

She had escaped these frightening seizures when she went to Baltimore from Oakland, and so had concluded that by activity she could put the demons to rout. London's weather, however, limited her activity. Even walking for any distance was out of the question since the poorly-lighted streets and dark alleys were favorite haunts of criminals. She felt Charles Dickens had described London well.

Gray foggy days followed each other in dreary succession until one afternoon Gertrude put her book aside, and pulling on a warm coat and muffler, stepped out into the street where a cold drizzling rain was falling. She wrapped the muffler close around her neck and slipped quietly into the stream of people who were gliding like specters through the foggy streets.

She was afraid in this Dante-like world where no one talked or laughed, but she was more afraid to stay inside where the dreadful feeling of desolation had at last caught up with her. For a while the crowd pushed her along faster and faster. Then she became aware of fewer people on the streets, then only an occasional passerby. Looking closely, Gertrude saw that the people she met wore ragged clothes and kept their eyes downcast. Was she in the slums? Leo had warned her to stay away from that sector of the city.

She was about to turn back when a commotion farther down the street caught her attention. Forgetting her fears for the moment, she walked toward the noise. As she drew nearer, she could see dirty poorly-clothed children fluttering excitedly about the outskirts of a crowd, chattering like birds, their shrill cries sharp against the fog.

Suddenly a high ethereal voice began to sing, "My name is Meg and the world is round. My name is Meg and the world is round." Overcome with curiosity, Gertrude pushed her way into the center of the crowd. There she saw a young girl no more than eight years old in a ragged red dress waving her thin white arms in the air as she sang over and over, "My name is Meg and the world is round." People laughed and threw pennies at her feet.

A wizened old hag grinned up at Gertrude. "Ain't the little tyke cute when she's drunk?"

"Drunk!" Gertrude shuddered. "Where does a child that age get enough to make her drunk?"

The old hag quit grinning and backed off. "She wants to know where she gets enough to make her drunk," she screeched, pointing a gnarled finger at Gertrude. "A rich goody-goody come down to do a little slummin' eh?"

Frightened eyes framed by cheap scarves and tattered caps turned on Gertrude. The hag darted toward the girl and grabbed her arm. "Oh Granma," the child wailed drunkenly, "didn't I sing pretty? You ain't goin' beat me, are you Granma?"

Gertrude watched the old woman drag the child through

a rickety doorway and disappear down a flight of stairs. The rest of the crowd quickly folded back into the shadows.

Standing alone on the sidewalk, Gertrude could still hear the child's haunting voice. Evil shadows seemed to be everywhere, flitting between her imagination and reality, but staying in neither place long enough to be identified. Turning back in the direction from which she had come, Gertrude walked rapidly away.

Why had she been so foolish as to let her mood drive her into the streets? The memory of the old woman's face leered menacingly before her. Gertrude shivered. If only she could see where she was going. Maybe she was walking deeper into the slums rather than toward Bloomsbury Square. Finally she saw a familiar landmark, and then another and another until at last she was opening the front door of their living quarters.

"Leo!" she called. But Leo was out. The rooms were as dark and unfriendly as when she left. Breathless and trembling, she went into the kitchen and fixed a pot of hot tea. As she drank the soothing liquid and tried to regain control of herself, she fixed her mind on America. Bright sunny America. England's weather was bad enough, but drunken children!

When Leo returned that evening, Gertrude had already booked passage on a boat leaving for America the following week.

"I think you're crazy!" Leo exclaimed when he heard her plans. "I *told* you to stay away from the slums. Besides, how would you get along in America? Here, by combining our incomes, we can be comfortable and even afford some luxuries. There you will have to take a job, something neither you nor I are suited for. Let's face it,

Gertrude, you and I are different from the rest of our family. Michael manages railroads; Simon is a gripman; even Bertha, now that she's married, works hard as a housewife; but you and I are productive only if we fill time in our own way."

Leo could say nothing that would dissuade Gertrude. When the day arrived for her boat to leave, she was on it.

She could hardly wait to be back in America. However, she dreaded the crossing, for she feared winter on the sea would be as bleak as London. Fortunately the sun shone brightly, firing the horizon with blazing colors in the morning and evening and beaming warmly down from its zenith at noon. Gertrude was so glad to see the sun that every day she lay in a deck chair and looked directly into it.

"Won't the sun damage your eyes?" asked a bearded young man who frequently sat in the chair next to hers.

"It hasn't yet," Gertrude answered abruptly, "and I've done it for as long as I can remember."

"Then you've experienced illumination?"

"Illumination?" Gertrude looked at him with interest.

"Students of Eastern philosophy aspire for it. I'm such a student myself. Once I attain it, I'm sure I can look into the sun, too."

"Oh," Gertrude chuckled, "*that* kind of illumination. "No, I haven't experienced it, nor do I wish to. I prefer straight-forward methodical thinking to a sudden burst of wisdom. And I like to clear my head the hard way, by *baking* out the mold and cobwebs."

six

"I have a country—America is my country, but Paris is my home town."

New York's skyline loomed large and sharply stylized against a crisp, blue winter sky. Gertrude stood on the upper deck of the boat and watched the land come close until she could see golden diamonds of sunlight dance brightly in the snow that lay everywhere on the docks and wharfs.

The invigorating air stirred her. She was eager to be settled on solid ground again. Then she could begin to write. In London she had concentrated on serious reading of sixteenth-century dramatists and eighteenth-century memoirs. Now she felt full of words and ideas and wanted to blaze her own path into style and composition.

Contrary to Leo's gloomy prediction, Gertrude found she didn't need a job to survive comfortably in New York. She arranged to share a house at 100th Street and Riverside Drive with three college friends, and her portion of the rent was reasonable. The house was large and attractive, surrounded by rose gardens and a gently sloping lawn that led to the Hudson River. Gertrude's needs were simple: time for working, space for walking, and plenty of food. For these accommodations her income was more than adequate.

She spent two days unpacking and arranging her books. Then with a burst of energy and confidence, she began to write, adhering to a strict schedule. Before long her work took shape as a psychological novel, *Quod Erat Demonstrandum*, in which she ruthlessly analyzed herself and the girls she lived with. She worked every day, taking copious notes and translating them into scenes. Although she was precise about the character traits of her housemates, she was honest to the point of severity about herself. "I always did thank God I wasn't born a woman," she wrote. And about a certain inertia that she recognized in herself, she said, "I want things . . . but only in order to understand them, and I never go and get them. I am a hopeless coward, I hate to risk hurting myself or anybody else."

Day after day she worked on the novel to the exclusion of practically everything else. No longer did she spend long hours at the opera or the art galleries. Nor did she take time out for lengthy intellectual discussions. Spring and summer passed, and it was late in October before she finished her book and put it away with no serious attempt at getting it published.

Working on this novel had shown her that what she must struggle to attain through writing was an expedient sense of time—specifically, to narrate the ongoing present, an idea that had come to her through William James. She hoped Leo's reaction to her work would be favorable when he came to visit over the Christmas holidays.

But Leo was destined not to arrive in New York that

year. As Gertrude learned later, he had left London and was journeying to America by way of Florence and Paris. On Christmas Eve he was having dinner in Paris with the cellist Pablo Casals when a compulsive urge to paint flooded over him. Rushing back to his hotel room, Leo stripped off his clothes and, sitting in front of a mirror, painted self-portraits all night long. The next morning he wrote a note to Gertrude:

> Gtde.,
> Inspiration, or something,
> has come to me. Cannot
> leave Paris.
> Leo

Another letter arrived some weeks later that told of Leo's finding living quarters in a two-story pavilion with a large atelier next to it in the courtyard at 27 Rue de Fleurus. The pavilion had four rooms with a kitchen and bath. The atelier, he said, was perfect for hanging the pictures he was purchasing. And as an added feature, the Luxembourg Gardens lay nearby. Why didn't Gertrude come to Paris and share the quarters with him?

Yes, Gertrude thought, why didn't she go to Paris? Now, with the novel done, there was nothing to keep her in New York. Besides, Michael and Sarah were living in Paris, too. They had gone for business reasons and had liked it so well they had stayed.

Childhood memories of Paris flashed through Gertrude's mind. It seemed only yesterday that she was clinging tightly to her mother's hand as they walked through the busy streets, going from one shop to another so Amelia could admire Parisian furs and perfumes. Gertrude marched smartly along beside her mother in a white dress with a red sash. On her feet she wore sturdy leather boots. She amused herself by bowing each time they passed a gentleman wearing a top hat and carrying a cane. She had loved living in Paris as a child. Perhaps she would as an adult, too.

Once more Gertrude crossed the ocean.

Soon after Gertrude arrived in Paris, she and Leo rearranged the decor of 27 Rue de Fleurus. Gertrude loved to fill spaces, and before long had every room crammed with figurines and sculptures she and Leo had collected in their travels through Italy. Leo hung his recently purchased paintings helter-skelter on the walls as the mood struck him. When they finished, the interior looked more like a museum than living quarters.

"You must hire a woman to clean and cook for you," Michael told them firmly. "You know you're not able to do it yourselves."

Gertrude and Leo agreed, for although Leo was a superb chef when it came to preparing exotic dishes, he couldn't cook simple food. Gertrude couldn't cook anything, and neither of them could clean or market well. Fortunately they found Hélène, whose abilities were nothing short of miraculous. Not only could she clean, cook, market, and conserve, she did it all with a dramatic flair that added a final touch of style to Gertrude's and Leo's Bohemian existence.

Gertrude loved her life in Paris. During the day she and Leo strolled through the streets wearing brown corduroy robes and sandals and looking for new art shows. Their appearance was so unusual that shop owners generally agreed they must be eccentric American millionaires.

In the evenings, they entertained guests who came to listen to Leo's latest theories of art. After the visitors left, which was sometimes in the early hours of the morning, Gertrude began to work.

She was involved in translating Gustave Flaubert's *Trois Contes* into English. An admirer of Flaubert's craftsmanship, she hoped that by working closely with his words she could learn how he so masterfully balanced characters, plot, and setting. She was near the end of her translation when she and Leo bought a painting by Paul Cézanne, who was to become her next great influence.

Leo had complained to Bernard Berenson that although he wanted more paintings, there were none of interest in Paris to buy. Berenson suggested that he look for the works of Paul Cézanne at a shop on Rue Lafitte owned by Ambroise Vollard. "Start by buying a landscape," Berenson advised.

Gertrude and Leo went at once to the shop. When they stepped inside, they were confronted by a large man with a dark foreboding face. "You are Ambroise Vollard?" Leo inquired.

The man nodded.

Gertrude looked around the shop. Paintings were strewn on the floor and stacked against the walls. Very few hung on the walls. When Vollard made no offer to help them, Leo said in a loud voice, "We have come to look at landscapes by a painter whose name is Cézanne."

At the mention of Cézanne's name, Vollard's face lighted up. "Ah yes, Cézanne," he said, rubbing his hands together. "Cézanne is very good. I will find one for you." He went up a flight of stairs and was gone a long time.

Finally he reappeared with a tiny painting of an apple. Most of the background was unpainted. Gertrude and Leo looked at it carefully, and then Leo said, "Yes, this is interesting, but what we want is a landscape."

Again Vollard climbed the stairs and returned with a Cézanne nude, but it showed only a woman's back.

"This is all?" asked Leo, "only a woman's back?"

Vollard nodded.

"But what we want to see is a *landscape*," Leo emphasized.

Once more Vollard went up the stairs. This time he struggled down with a very large canvas, which he sat in front of Gertrude and Leo.

"Oh yes," said Leo. "Now we are agreeing. I see that this painting has a landscape in it, but such a small portion of one. Couldn't we see a landscape that is larger than a postage stamp?"

"Yes, of course," Vollard said, and climbed the stairs again.

By that time the deep shadows of late afternoon filled the shop. No sooner had Vollard disappeared from sight than an aged charwoman made her way down the stairs. "Good night, Sir and Madame," she said to Gertrude and Leo and went out the door. After a while another charwoman made her way down the stairs and murmured, "Good night, Sir and Madame," and went out the door. Gertrude burst out laughing.

"Why are you laughing?"

"Cézanne doesn't exist, Leo. Vollard doesn't understand us, so he goes upstairs and tells these old women what to paint. They don't understand him, and so they paint what they want to and he brings it down to show us and says it is a Cézanne!"

Before Leo could answer, Vollard was standing in front of them once more. In his hand he held a small green landscape. "This is exactly what we want," Leo cried when he saw it, "a small canvas, a small landscape."

"Lucky for him the last old lady painted what we wanted before she left," Gertrude whispered to Leo, and they both burst out laughing.

Vollard scowled and looked annoyed.

"We will buy this painting," said Leo, and a price was agreed upon. They paid the amount and left the shop.

With this purchase, Gertrude became as enthusiastic about paintings as Leo. They spent the rest of the winter buying all the pictures they could afford: a Daumier, a Manet, two Renoirs, two small Cézanne nudes, a Toulouse-Lautrec, a Manguin, an El Greco, and some Gauguins. Although they paid only thirty or forty dollars for some of the pictures, by the end of the winter they decided they could afford only one more. Then they must stop. They looked and looked, finally deciding upon a portrait of Madame Cézanne.

To their great disappointment, the price was higher than they expected. They didn't have enough money. But Michael heard of their plight and advanced them enough to cover the amount. Soon the portrait was hanging at 27 Rue de Fleurus.

Gertrude spent hours in front of the portrait of Madame Cézanne. She was working on a trilogy portraying the lives of three ordinary women, *The Good Anna*, *Gentle Lena*, and *Melanctha*. By studying Cézanne's composition she hoped to write portraits in the same manner he painted them—realistically, with the impression of a moving center.

Leo resented Gertrude's attention to Cézanne and also her driving ambition to become a writer. He was used to her sympathizing with him and supporting his ambitions, not her own. The deeper Gertrude withdrew into her own world, the more sullen Leo became. Late one afternoon, when Gertrude had spent an unusually long time in front of the portrait, Leo exploded, "You fool yourself if you think you can learn style and composition by studying Cézanne."

Gertrude looked at him with a start, then turned back to the painting. "No, Leo, I don't fool myself," she said.

"I say you do! What have you learned? Nothing as far as I can see. Those three silly vignettes you're writing sound like the ramblings of a naive child. If any of our friends were to read them, they would think you witless and I half-witted for not stopping you."

Gertrude's brown eyes flashed with anger, but she said quietly, "You are the one who fools himself, Leo. You object to my writing because if I should be successful it would be a threat to you."

"Threat to me!" Leo shouted. "Have you gone soft-headed that you think you could ever compete with me? Where would you be if it weren't for the ideas germinated in my brain that inevitably you take as your own? I am the one who establishes a life pattern, and you fall into it."

"Mademoiselle–Monsieur . . ." Hélène called from the kitchen. "Shall I pour wine for dinner?"

Leo and Gertrude stared angrily at each other.

"Mademoiselle–Monsieur . . ." Hélène called again.

"Yes, pour wine," Leo shouted back, "lots of it!"

As Gertrude looked at Leo's angry face and heard his harsh voice, she felt a unique psychological process stirring inside her, as if a cord that had bound them together since childhood had snapped. Suddenly Leo put his arm out for her to take. "All right, we've had our little spat," he said crossly. "Let's forget about it now and have dinner."

Gertrude put her hand on Leo's arm, but it wasn't the familiar arm she had leaned on for so many years. Without a word they went into dinner. As Gertrude sat down and looked across the table at Leo, she felt a pang of regret and wished they hadn't argued. She liked things around her to be familiar, and now things were different. It was a bother to think of Leo in a different way and to think of herself in relation to Leo in a different way. "I do hate change in my daily living," she admitted to herself.

"To the future." Leo proposed the toast.

"To the future!" Gertrude responded.

seven

Matisse laughed, "I am an artist. What other things I am are determined by the weather and the day."

Time temporarily healed Gertrude's and Leo's quarrel, at least to outward appearances. Gertrude tried to show more interest in Leo's work, and Leo tempered his criticism of Gertrude's writing. They told themselves that their angry words were only natural. After all, they were both high strung and artistic. A spat now and then meant nothing.

In an effort to improve their relationship, they began attending as many art shows as they could, for seeing pictures was a passion they both shared, and they loved to gossip afterward about the painters and the paintings shown. One of these shows was the *Salon d'Automne* of 1905.

"Let's find Michael and Sarah," Leo suggested as he and Gertrude made their way through the crowd.

"There they are," Gertrude said, spotting Sarah's fashionable hat. Michael was standing nearby. As Gertrude and

Leo came closer, they could hear Sarah talking excitedly to the group around her.

"I've never seen such behavior—it's animalistic!"

"What's animalistic?" asked Leo.

"Oh Leo," Sarah said breathlessly, "have you seen *La Femme au Chapeau* by the artist Matisse?"

"Yes, we saw it."

"And did you see how people were trying to scratch off the paint because they disliked it?"

"Yes."

"I think it's bestial!"

"Interesting you should use that word. People are calling Matisse and those who follow him *Les Fauves*, apparently because they paint with such violent colors."

"What does Matisse think of that, of his group being called 'the beasts'?" Michael asked.

"I've heard he's very happy about it. He likes having started such a movement."

"Matisse has started no movement!" Gertrude countered emphatically. "When a man comes along who produces something so true and communicable that many people are affected, then *that* is the beginning of a movement. Matisse has done no such thing. Just look at his paintings, *La Femme au Chapeau*, for example. Do you feel any depth of communication in it? I don't. The only value I see in that painting is in owning it. I think we should buy it."

Leo stared at Gertrude for a minute, then his face broke into smiles. "Of course!" he exclaimed. "It would be a sensational painting to own. Let's find the secretary of the Gallery."

"Monsieur Matisse is asking five hundred francs for *La Femme au Chapeau*," the secretary told them.

"We will pay four hundred francs," Leo said.

"I will contact Monsieur Matisse and notify you of his decision tomorrow."

But Gertrude and Leo were so eager to conclude the transaction that they didn't wait to be notified. Early the next morning they returned. The secretary shook his head. "Monsieur Matisse is standing firm. Five hundred francs or nothing."

"We *must* have that painting," Gertrude whispered to Leo.

"Very well," Leo said to the secretary, "we will pay five hundred francs."

As owners of *La Femme au Chapeau*, Gertrude and Leo became celebrities. Although their previous picture collection had brought many people to 27 Rue de Fleurus, the number who now came was so great that Gertrude found it difficult to write.

"I can't work," she complained to Leo. "We must invite people to come only at certain times and let it be known they won't be welcome otherwise. Let's set aside Saturday nights and entertain with dinner and a salon gathering afterward."

Leo liked being lionized as the owner of a unique art collection and wasn't as eager as Gertrude to limit their visitors, but he finally consented. Together they made out a list for the next Saturday night, inviting Matisse as the the guest of honor.

Matisse came, flanked on either side by Michael and Sarah, who had become much interested in his paintings. The other guests were famous or aspiring-to-be-famous Paris artists. Gertrude and Leo, comfortably dressed as ever in their robes and sandals, were their usual charming selves as hosts. They mingled easily with the guests, encouraging conversation and tossing out bits of gossip.

"Oh Monsieur Matisse," Gertrude called as their guests were leaving. "May I see you at your studio next week?"

"Of course, Mademoiselle Stein," Matisse answered. "You must wear warm clothes, though, for my studio is very cold. But," he added brightly, "I have a marvelous view of Notre Dame that I will show you."

"Good, I will come Wednesday at three in the afternoon."

The next Wednesday at three promptly, Gertrude knocked at Matisse's door. It was opened by a dark-haired, very efficient looking woman. "Mademoiselle Stein?"

"Yes."

"I am Madame Matisse. My husband is waiting for you." A small thin girl stood behind Madame Matisse. Gertrude caught a glimpse of the rooms beyond and saw they were sparsely furnished, but impressively clean. Gertrude went immediately up the stairs that Madame Matisse indicated led to her husband's studio and again knocked on a door.

"Come in," Matisse called cheerfully.

Gertrude opened the door to find Matisse dressed in coat and mittens and painting a very large canvas with the same bold colors he had used in *La Femme au Chapeau.*

"Ah, Mademoiselle Stein," Matisse said, putting down his paint brush and taking Gertrude's arm, "come at once and see the view of Notre Dame from my window."

"But you shouldn't stop painting," Gertrude protested.

"Oh yes, I stop painting many times a day to revere this grand cathedral. See, look at it there."

From the window Gertrude saw a breathtaking view of Notre Dame's thirteenth-century towers thrusting themselves powerfully and majestically into the cold bleak afternoon. "It makes me think of courage," she said.

"It remainds me of Our Lady," Matisse said quietly.

Gertrude looked at him quickly, but saw no hint of embarrassment in his eyes. "You are religious?"

Matisse laughed. "I am an artist. What other things I am are determined by the weather and the day. Today it is cold, and I am keeping warm by playing the clown with my orange and red paints."

"But doesn't seeing Notre Dame every day inspire you to work?"

"No," Matisse said, splashing paint on his canvas, "I am inspired by the thinness of my wife and child. My wife tries hard to stretch a franc and does better than most, but there are very few francs in our household these days. That's why Michael and Sarah suggested that I start a school for painters. They thought you and Leo might help finance it. I hope that is why you came to see me."

Gertrude pulled her collar close around her neck. She was very cold. "No, I came to satisfy myself about you and *Les Fauves*, and to decide whether or not I could concede that you had started a movement."

Matisse looked at her curiously, "I'm afraid I don't understand."

"No, of course not," Gertrude said impatiently. "Now, regarding the school. Why do you start a school? If you are serious about painting, you wouldn't think of such a thing. Besides, how can you teach other people when you're not an artist yourself yet? I think you have lost your head because people are beginning to know your name. But remember, they know your name only because you paint scandalously, not because you paint well."

Matisse had stopped painting and listened intently to what Gertrude was saying. When she finished, he shook his head sadly. "You do not understand, Mademoiselle. I want to be an artist, and a profound one. But I am also a father whose undernourished child needs food. With a school, I can continue to paint and feed her at the same time."

"You lack courage, Monsieur," Gertrude said, rising to go. "I am greatly disappointed."

"You do not know," Matisse said, somewhat angry, "what it is to have a hungry child. I doubt very much if you know what it is to be hungry yourself."

"I know what it is to be hungry," Gertrude responded, going toward the door. "But the food I crave is the substance of genius."

"You think you are a *genius*?"

"I *know* I am," Gertrude said, going out the door. "Good day, Monsieur Matisse."

On her way down the stairs, Gertrude nodded briefly to Madame Matisse and walked out into the cold afternoon. A French woman passed, her threadbare coat pulled tightly across her hunched shoulders. French women always look old in winter, Gertrude thought, because they bend and shiver in the cold. She straightened her shoulders and inhaled deeply. She didn't want to look old–ever! Invigorated by the quick intake of air, she decided to go to Sagot's, one of her favorite art dealers.

Walking briskly, she was soon inside the warm shop.

"Mademoiselle Stein!" Sagot greeted her. "How good that you should come on such a wintry afternoon to buy pictures."

"I have only come to look, Sagot."

"As long as you wish. But there are so many beautiful paintings here that you will be tempted to buy one, maybe two."

Gertrude smiled. "No, today I will only look."

"*Oui*, Mademoiselle."

Next to Sagot stood a short young man with a shock of brown hair that fell over his forehead. For a minute Gertrude was held by his compelling brown eyes, then she began digging through the many stacks of canvases.

The shop was small, and since there were no other customers, it was very quiet. As Gertrude searched for something unique, she couldn't help overhearing the conversation between the two men.

"Who is that?" the young man asked, apparently making no effort to keep his voice down.

"Gertrude Stein," Sagot answered quietly. "She and her brother Leo are Americans who like to buy pictures—many pictures. They are among my best customers. Mademoiselle Stein," Sagot said, lowering his voice even more, "buys with an eye for the abstract, for the spirit behind the painting. Monsieur buys art for its concrete value. But between them they own some of the most talked-about paintings in Paris today. I will introduce you, then you can go see their collection for yourself."

"No, no," the young man said impatiently. "I have no interest in her art collection. What a magnificent head she has! I would like her to pose for me. Would you ask her after I leave?"

"But," said Sagot, astonished, "I haven't known you to use a model since you arrived in Paris."

"Please ask her."

"*Oui*, Monsieur Picasso."

Having looked at all the canvases she cared to see, and certainly not wanting to model for anyone, Gertrude left the shop before Sagot could approach her.

Walking home she mused to herself. So an artist wanted

her to model for him because of her head! She chuckled at the thought of it. The name Picasso sounded familiar though. Where had she heard it? Of course! The signature "Pablo Picasso" was on the last painting Leo had bought, *Young Girl with a Basket of Flowers*. She didn't like the picture. Something about the legs and feet of the girl repelled her.

That evening Leo arrived home tired but excited. He threw himself into a comfortable chair near Gertrude's desk. "What an afternoon this has been," he said. "You'll never guess who H. P. Roché introduced me to."

"Who?" Gertrude answered, hardly looking up from her writing. H. P. Roché liked to know everyone. There could be no guessing who his latest conquest might be.

"Picasso!" Leo shot back, eager to tell his news. "We went to his studio and saw his works. He's just finished what he calls the Pink Period. Paintings all done in predominantly pink tones."

"Picasso!"

Leo looked at Gertrude curiously. "You're even more surprised than I thought you'd be. But imagine, meeting him so soon after buying his picture! Such energy he has —strong creative energy. Dark hair and dark eyes. Mark my words, he's going to be one of the great painters of this age."

"You think he's *that* good?"

"Of course he is, but here's a surprise for you. When I told him my name, he began jabbering in Spanish and gesticulating all over the place. It was hard to calm him down. But Roché finally made *him* understand that *we* weren't understanding, and he spoke in French again. The gist of what he said was that he had seen you somewhere and since I was your brother, would I ask you to model for him. He thinks you have a magnificent head. Now . . . what do you think of that?"

"I think he's crazy," Gertrude said flatly. "He would have to be crazy to want me to model for him. Besides, anyone who draws feet as prehensile-looking as those in *Young Girl wtih a Basket of Flowers* is not going to draw my head."

Leo said nothing for a few minutes, but Gertrude could sense he was getting angry. Finally he exploded, "Why do you always have to be so stubborn?"

"Why are *you* so angry?"

"Because I've invited Picasso for dinner next Saturday night. What's going to happen when I tell him you think his paintings are terrible?"

"If he has any critical eye at all, he'll agree with me!"

eight

"You are essentially comic and I am essentially tragic,"
Picasso would tell her sadly.

By six o'clock the next Saturday evening, 27 Rue de Fleurus was full of guests. Many of them Gertrude had never seen before. Drawing Leo away from a full-bosomed, very tailored woman, she quietly inquired, "Who invited all these people?"

"We did."

"No, no, *we* didn't. I invited only four."

"And I invited only seven. Oh well, now that they're in, let them stay. Have you met Picasso yet?"

"Is he here?"

"He must be. I heard him laugh a minute ago, but I haven't caught sight of him. Lord! There must be over twenty people here."

"How do you know it was Picasso laughing?" Gertrude asked.

"When he laughs he makes a high whinnying sound. Very peculiar. You can't mistake it."

Just then Hélène touched Gertrude on the elbow. "Mademoiselle, dinner is ready to be served."

"Why Hélène, you are positively *red*!"

"*Oui*," Hélène said, wiping a wilted sleeve across her perspiring forehead. "There are so many guests . . . Oh Mademoiselle," she wailed, "I'm afraid the beautiful dinner I had planned is ruined. There are twice as many people as I expected. I tried to make more food, but I added so much that I quite forgot where I started and where I left off."

"I'm sure the dinner's fine, Hélène," Gertrude said, taking her by the arm. "But just to make sure, I'll go into the kitchen with you and taste it. Seat our guests while I'm gone," she whispered to Leo. "Next Saturday night, *no one* gets in unless we know him."

When Gertrude came to the table, the guests were all seated. She quickly found a chair for herself and sat down so Hélène could begin serving. The unexpected confusion made Gertrude's appetite even bigger than usual. Paying little attention to people sitting near her, she ate with gusto. A plate of bread was placed in front of her, and soon she had devoured all but one crust. As she reached for the remaining piece, another hand clamped over hers. Startled, she looked into two angry brown eyes. She recognized them as the same brown eyes that had held her at Sagot's–Picasso's.

"*That* piece of bread," he said, "is mine!"

For a minute, Gertrude didn't relinquish her hold. Then she withdrew and, throwing her head back, laughed merrily. Picasso stared at her, then he too threw back his head and laughed. "Mademoiselle Stein," he said, putting out his hand, "I congratulate you on your tremendous appetite."

"Monsieur Picasso," Gertrude replied, accepting his handshake, "I congratulate you on your courage."

"I want you to model for me," Picasso said at once. "Didn't your brother tell you? I sent the message by him and thought I would get an answer before this."

"Yes, he told me. Of course I won't model for you. It's out of the question."

"Why do you say this?"

"Because I don't like your paintings; I find them repulsive, unnatural."

"What do you mean?"

"I mean you paint ugly feet."

Picasso's eyes flashed angrily for a minute. Then a smile broke across his face, and he howled with laughter. "Yes, you are right," he said finally, "but you will see—when I paint your head, it will not be ugly. Your face will be elongated with classic lines and planes to highlight and give strength. Shall we start tomorrow?"

"No, no! I tell you, I don't want to model. It would bore me to sit and do nothing. I would be disgruntled for days."

"We will talk; we will discuss. Let's begin tomorrow at two o'clock. If you feel disgruntled at the end of an hour, we will stop." With a great deal of reluctance, Gertrude finally agreed.

Shortly before two the next afternoon, she found Picasso's studio in a run-down building on the Rue Ravignan. A tall, very beautiful woman answered her knock. "Gertrude Stein?"

"Yes."

"I am Fernande."

Gertrude stepped through the door into an apartment filled with clutter and confusion. Sunday papers were strewn over the floor and it seemed there were dogs everywhere, running over the furniture, knocking things down, and barking in excited little yips. Picasso appeared and began yelling commands at the dogs, but his high-strung energy incited them to even greater activity. Fernande smiled at Gertrude and motioned her to a chair.

Picasso said something that Gertrude couldn't understand, and so she shook her head. This seemed to infuriate him, and he began speaking very rapidly in Spanish. Fernande immediately followed suit, gesticulating and speaking as rapidly in French as Picasso was in Spanish.

"Come into the studio!" Picasso yelled in Gertrude's ear, and grabbing her by the arm, he pulled her with him. Once inside the studio, he kicked at the dogs to keep them out and slammed the door. Smiling sheepishly, he said, "The dogs are excited to see new people."

"Yes," Gertrude replied, "I can see that."

Pulling a broken armchair out from a pile of junk in the corner, Picasso motioned for Gertrude to sit down. "I will sketch you sitting here," he said. "To entertain you, I will tell you of my history." Snatching up a drawing sheet, he climbed up on a high stool and began making quick strokes. "I was born," he began, his staccato speech keeping time with his sketching movements, "in Málaga, Spain, the son of a Basque drawing teacher . . ." Before Gertrude knew it, an hour had passed.

"Are you disgruntled as you said you would be?" Picasso inquired.

"No," Gertrude replied, and certainly she wasn't. Picasso's extraordinary aliveness struck a responsive chord in her. The session lasted late into the afternoon.

Finally Picasso put his drawing sheet away. "The modeling is over for now," he said, "but you will come again?"

"Yes, I will come again."

Gertrude looked forward to modeling for Picasso. When she and Leo had traveled in Spain, she had loved the Spanish character, and now she could observe it in Paris by knowing Picasso. He carried about him everything she cared for in Spain, the landscape, the architecture, and the basically tragic Spanish nature.

"You are essentially comic, and I am essentially tragic," Picasso would tell her sadly. Gertrude always laughed when he said this and reminded him that he shouldn't be sad, he should be happy. They should both be happy for, after all, they were artists, and being such they could experience the daily miracle—the miracle of creation. Picasso would shake his head and say he didn't believe it to be a miracle at all, rather he thought it a lot of hard work.

Gertrude saw more and more of Picasso. Their minds raced and clicked along together. Since Leo was not interested in Gertrude's writing, she turned to Picasso with ideas. His insight and magnificent energy provided just the spur she needed to regain the self-confidence Leo had come close to destroying. Under the influence of Picasso's friendship, her writing proceeded rapidly, and soon she finished the stories of *The Good Anna*, *The Gentle Lena*, and *Melanctha*.

Sarah read the manuscript and praised it highly. Leo read it and pronounced it "garbage." Picasso couldn't comment because he didn't read English, but he did remark about Leo's reaction. "Leo does not think your writing is bad; he is jealous of our friendship. I see it in his eyes. He is acting like a child. Pay no attention to him."

Yet it was difficult for Gertrude to ignore Leo, for he

went out of his way to be critical about her ambitions and, now, also about Picasso's. He seldom painted, nor did he read. Most of the time he stalked about the apartment looking like a black cloud and making unkind remarks about Picasso.

"I thought you liked him," Gertrude would counter. "You said he was going to be one of the great painters of our time."

"I was deceived!"

Returning from a long walk one day, Leo suddenly suggested that they invite Picasso for tea some afternoon. Surprised and wary, Gertrude passed the invitation on.

"No, I will not go," Picasso said, his short body taut. "He wants to kill me."

"Picasso, he doesn't want to kill you. He wants to talk about art, about your painting method."

"It is a trick. I think your brother is insane."

"No, he is not insane. Maybe he's decided to like you. We should give him a chance."

"Gertrude, you are thirty-one."

"Yes."

"I am twenty-four. You have lived seven years longer than I. Maybe when I am thirty-one, I, too, will be ready to die. But at twenty-four, I do not want to die."

"You are being a Spaniard, Pablo, and a melodramatic one. If you will come, I promise that he won't kill you."

Finally Picasso gave in. Reluctant and a little angry with Gertrude for prompting him, he arrived punctually at the appointed time. Leo answered the door, greeting him warmly, "Pablo Picasso! You have stayed away a long time."

"Yes, but maybe not long enough."

"Nonsense," Leo said laughing, "come in and have some tea. We'll gossip so I can catch up on your activities, and then I want to hear about your work—Gertrude never mentions it."

As Hélène served tea and small pastries, Leo seemed high-spirited and cheerful. Picasso and Gertrude were quiet and watchful. "Now," Leo said, taking a last drink from his cup, "I would like to speak with you, Picasso. I have some things to tell you." Picasso and Gertrude cast startled looks at each other.

Leo banged his cup into the saucer. "What's going on between you two? If I didn't know better, I would think you were lovers from the way you've behaved this afternoon. I don't want to know your intentions, Pablo, I just want to talk about some of your recent paintings." Sighing and throwing up his hands in a Spanish gesture of despair, Picasso followed Leo into the next room. Leo closed the door behind them.

Gertrude was uneasy. Although she was certain that her brother would never commit a macabre act, she was equally certain that by being truculent and caustic he could inflame the already edgy Picasso into a rage. If this were to happen, the result, she knew, would not be pleasant.

She tried to read, but found she couldn't concentrate. Her eyes wandered to the closed door. Suddenly the door burst open and Picasso stormed out, his eyes shooting fire. Behind him Gertrude caught a glimpse of Leo, red-faced and sputtering. He grabbed the open door and slammed it with such force that the pictures on the wall swung crazily. Some of them crashed to the floor.

"I told you," Picasso screamed at Gertrude over his

shoulder as he left the apartment, "your brother is insane. He criticized *my* painting. He tried to tell *me* how to paint. He is insane!"

Hélène appeared from the kitchen, nervously wiping her hands on her apron. "What is the commotion, Mademoiselle? Why is Monsieur Picasso yelling?"

"Monsieur Picasso and Leo had a disagreement," Gertrude said shortly. "Please re-hang the pictures, Hélène."

Gertrude went to Leo's door and knocked loudly. The door flew open. "What do you want?" Leo growled.

"You must apologize to Pablo. He was a guest. You knew he would be angry if you criticized his work, and yet that seems to have been the purpose of your invitation. You must go to him and apologize." Once more the door slammed, and once more pictures shook dizzily.

"What is happening in this house?" Hélène cried.

"I think," Gertrude said, as she stormed out of the room, "that Leo shut the door so loudly he made the sky fall over him and me. Take care of the pictures, Hélène. I'm going to the atelier to write."

nine

"You don't understand, Leo. There is a beauty here, a kind of savage beauty that must be seen with the mind."

Gertrude wrote feverishly all night long in an attempt to shut out the unpleasant scenes of the previous afternoon. When dawn came, she was shaking with fatigue. Hélène knocked lightly on the atelier door.

"Mademoiselle."

"Yes."

"I have your morning coffee."

"Bring it in, please."

Suddenly Gertrude heard Michael's voice outside the apartment, tense and commanding. "Leo! Gertrude!"

Gertrude started toward the door, but Hélène was ahead of her. Ignoring Hélène's gentle greeting, Michael pushed her aside and burst out, "Gertrude, have you heard the news?"

"What news?"

"San Francisco's been hit by an earthquake."

"An earthquake! Oh my Lord! Hélène, quickly, go wake Leo."

"From the reports," Michael said, running his hand across his balding head, "San Francisco's devastated. Fires, whole buildings crumbling. Most of the city has had to evacuate, and they're not sure it's over yet. Sarah and I must leave as soon as possible to check on our investments."

Before Michael finished his sentence, Leo came hurrying in, hastily wrapping his dressing gown around him. "Hélène told me about the earthquake," he said, as Michael started to speak. "But my God, if you go to San Francisco, what will happen to our income flats here in Paris?"

"That's what I came about. Get something to write on, and I'll give you instructions for managing them."

Still groggy from sleep, Leo fumbled through stacks of papers on the table, finally coming up with a blank one. Across the top he wrote, April 19, 1906. "When did the earthquake hit?" he asked.

"Last night. I just received word a short time ago."

Gertrude put on a light coat and went out the door, her tiredness forgotten for the moment. She wasn't needed at home, but she would be needed at Michael's apartment. Sarah would be in a state! As she walked through the early morning streets toward 58 Rue Madame, she thought about nature and how it sometimes required an upheaval to restore balance. The same was true of people, too. Surely she and Leo would find some equilibrium soon. Their lives had been eruptive long enough.

When Sarah answered Gertrude's knock, she was close to tears. "Oh Gertrude," she burst out, "what am I to do? I don't want to go to San Francisco and leave all our wonderful paintings in the care of strangers."

"No, of course you don't," Gertrude assured her, "and you won't have to. Leo can help you crate the small Matisses that you like so much, and you can take them with you. While you're away, Leo and I will look after the rest of your paintings."

Gertrude's ready answer and commanding presence calmed Sarah. After a cup of hot tea, Sarah felt strong enough to begin packing. Gertrude didn't help, she only watched; for as she often explained to people, what was commonly known as work she couldn't do.

Within days the packing was finished and the apartment closed. Michael and Sarah were ready to sail. "We won't stay any longer than we have to," Michael promised Gertrude as he told her goodbye.

"Please don't!" Gertrude pleaded.

She would miss Michael. She relied on him not only for financial support and advice, but also, as her father had predicted many years before, for his common sense in daily affairs. And so did Leo. Gertrude dreaded to think how gloomy Leo would be without Michael to help keep his spirits lifted.

Before a week had passed, the very thing Gertrude feared began to happen. Leo became more and more irritable. He disliked the responsibility of managing the family income in Paris because such work annoyed him. Furthermore, it took him away from his real calling, which he now declared was in the field of criticism.

"Criticism!" Gertrude exclaimed. "I thought you were determined to be a great painter."

"Painting is out of the question," Leo answered. "Every time I pick up a brush I come face to face with my own confusion and frustration, and then I have the devil to pay by suffering those damnable stomach pains that attack me. Only yesterday I tried to paint, and last night I had such pains and nightmares I thought I would die. I dreamed that

Father was reprimanding me, upbraiding me in his usual tyrannical manner. I *hated* him. I awoke in a pool of sweat. I tell you, *Father* is the root of all my unhappiness. He's to blame for my inability to produce creatively, not I."

Gertrude listened to Leo's outburst in amazement. She had disliked their father, it was true, but she had no such feelings of hatred for him. Leo looked at her, waiting for some kind of response. Getting none, he buried his face in his hands.

"I think it would be wise for us to leave Paris this summer," Gertrude said quietly, "and go to Casa Ricci in Fiesole." The two had rented the house before, on an earlier trip to Italy.

Leo looked up with a flicker of gratitude. "Yes," he said, "let's! Maybe the change will help. I'll make some arrangement about the flats."

Gertrude held little hope that a change would lift Leo's depression, but she was pleasantly surprised. Within a month after they had arrived in Fiesole, he was more lighthearted than she had seen him for years. "I will be well before you know it," he told her. "Hot sun, fresh air, and good food are what I need." During the day he tramped around the countryside, coming in red-faced and full of life. At night he read to Gertrude, and the two of them laughed over humorous passages and wept if a scene was sad.

Every minute Leo was away during the day, Gertrude worked, and always she worked at night after he stopped reading. She had sent her trilogy of stories, which she entitled *Three Histories*, to Pitts-Duffield Publishing Company in New York. The manuscript had been returned with a note saying the work was much too unconventional and too literary for Pitts-Duffield to consider publishing.

Far from being discouraged about this rejection, Gertrude was spurred to even greater effort, for the more she wrote, the more convinced she was of her own literary genius. Now she was working on a book that was entitled *The Making of Americans*, a commentary on psychological types, combined with all the known history of the Stein family.

As summer drew to an end, Leo announced himself cured. "I want to go back to Paris and paint," he said. "Not a ripple of pain for over two months, and I'm full of robust good spirits." Gertrude wanted to return to Paris, too, because Paris provoked deliberation in her writing, something she now needed. Eagerly they gathered up their belongings.

After arriving at 27 Rue de Fleurus, Gertrude gladly let Hélène do the unpacking so she could turn her full attention to *The Making of Americans*. Night after night she wrote, surrounded by stacks of papers filled with her scrawling handwriting. The work was growing into a staggering opus. Words spilled out all over each other, and still she couldn't write enough to empty the fullness of her creative urge. She stopped only when her hand became so tired she couldn't decipher her own script. But her mind continued to race, and she cursed her physical limitations. Each morning she reluctantly put her pen down and went to bed. Sinking into an oblivion of deep exhaustion, she slept until early afternoon. When she awakened, she ate ravenously, read for several hours, took a walk, ate more, then went back to her desk to begin again.

So involved had she become with her writing, that she saw no one, not even Picasso. One day he burst into the apartment. "Gertrude!" he cried. "I have waited to hear that you had returned, but no word. Yesterday I saw Leo on the street, and so today I come here. Why didn't you notify me you were back?"

"Pablo!" Gertrude said, embracing him warmly. "How brown you are from your summer in Spain. Ah, I see in your eyes that you have been inspired. Someday you will know how right I have been when I tell you that it is Spain that nourishes you—and what appreciation do you give it? None! You suckle it as you would a mother, and then you turn your back on it."

Picasso's brown eyes flashed with pleasure at Gertrude's scolding. "Yes, yes, Gertrude, I am bad, and I will come to no good end. But now, you must come to my apartment. I have a surprise."

On the way to his studio, Picasso chattered incessantly. He was magnetic and alive, full of verve and excitement. He talked about how well his painting was going and how he had become fascinated by pre-Roman Iberian sculpture. "What have you done that shows it?" Gertrude asked.

"You'll see," Picasso replied, holding open the door of his apartment for her.

Fighting off the usual barrage of yapping dogs, Picasso directed Gertrude to the studio and slammed the door behind them. "There," he said, pointing to a canvas in the middle of the room, "you see—*that* shows the influence of Iberian sculpture."

Gertrude stared. There in front of her was the portrait that she had spent so many hours sitting for. At first she neither liked nor disliked it, rather it compelled an intellectual reaction. Done mostly in browns, the lines of her face were linear and rigid, framing unseeing, stylized eyes. In spite of this, her face was expressive; she looked wise, sphinx-like, as if she contained the riddles and answers to the universe. Only in the body was there movement, but

Gertrude was shocked at how masculine the movement seemed.

Picasso sat cross-legged on a window ledge and watched her. She turned to him. "This is not a physical portrait of me. This is what *you* see, the inside, the outside, the mind, the emotions–everything!"

"Yes," Picasso answered, almost defiantly, "do you like it?"

"I think what you say about me in this painting is true. Yes, I like it. It is a masterpiece!"

Picasso jumped off the window ledge, his face flushed with excitement. "You are right. And one that must be seen with the mind."

"But how did you finish it, Pablo? You hadn't painted in the head when I left at the beginning of last summer."

"When I returned from Spain, I came at once to the studio and painted the head from memory."

Gertrude turned back to the portrait. She looked at it for a long time. Finally she said, almost to herself, "Tomorrow I will bring Leo."

"He will not like it."

"No, but I will bring him anyway."

The next afternoon Gertrude and Leo went to see the portrait. Leo had been in excellent spirits since his return to Paris, but the idea of seeing Picasso again made his old irritability return. When Picasso opened the studio door for them, Leo looked disdainful and pedagogical. Such a pontifical manner ignited a spark in Picasso's explosive nature. Abruptly he gestured across the room. "There," he said, "is the painting."

Adjusting his monocle, Leo began to examine the portrait. At last he stepped back. "It doesn't look like Gertrude."

"Never mind," Picasso replied, "it will!"

Leo looked frigid. "What a terrible thing to say, Pablo. This portrait is harsh, ugly. The lines of Gertrude's physique are soft. You should have made gentle folds. Is this what your friendship amounts to that you should produce something so uncomplimentary?"

Quickly Gertrude interfered. "You don't understand, Leo. There is a beauty here, a kind of savage beauty that must be seen with the mind. Besides, Pablo has said many times that one who creates is forced by the very struggle of the task to produce a certain ugliness, or at least it seems ugly to those who observe it for the first time. But what seems ugly is the crash of creation, the splitting apart of reality. Look at the portrait again and you will see what I say is true. You must recondition your senses and your mind to perceive a new kind of beauty."

Leo put his monocle away and sat down in the broken armchair that Gertrude had used while posing for the portrait. "You are crazy, both of you. God knows where it will lead if you continue to pursue these neurotic impulses of yours. You conceive of something in your brain and then decide it is so. Blind courage does not make art!"

"It does," Gertrude replied quietly, "if one is a genius."

"A genius? Gertrude, you *are* crazy! I could weep for you. While we were in Fiesole you were reasonable, and we could talk. But when you see Picasso again, you lose your senses and you lose me. I am *sane*, and I need for you to be, too."

"You may be sane, Leo, but you are self-centered and shackled to conventional thinking. You haven't the courage to dream, to experiment, to shatter the delusion we call reality by living in the present moment without benefit of memory, or tradition, or a preconceived notion of what should be. You are afraid to enter the *real* world of timelessness and immediate meaning." Breathless, Gertrude stopped. She was surprised to discover how angry she was, and how vitriolic her voice sounded. Leo lowered his eyes and was quiet.

Finally Picasso said, "Let's not talk any more. We will all follow our destinies, Gertrude. There is no need to bludgeon Leo's emotions because he doesn't see as we do. I will pour some wine, and we will drink together."

Leo's hand was trembling when he accepted the cup of strong-bodied red wine from Picasso. Gertrude remained quiet, stolid, watching Leo. "Let's laugh now," Picasso proposed, "let's drink to laughter." They all raised their glasses, but they didn't laugh. They drank in silence. Leo sipped his wine slowly and then left the studio.

"You were hard on him," Picasso said to Gertrude. "It is sad to see that soon you will not care for each other at all."

"He was hard on me," Gertrude answered in an edgy, defiant voice. "He has been hard on me ever since I wrote my first story and showed it to him. From that time on he has tried to destroy my will to create. I'm not sorry for what I said today. I will not be stopped by his jealousy. It takes courage, Pablo, to believe in yourself and to be devoted to your own pure thinking. I have the courage—Leo hasn't. I will succeed, but he will fail. He knows this."

Picasso looked into his cup of wine. "You sadden me, Gertrude, when you talk this way."

"You sadden me, too, Pablo, when I know that not even you understand."

Gertrude got up to leave. "*Au revoir*, Pablo."

"*Au revoir*, my Gertrude."

ten

"Who *is Alice B. Toklas?*"

Michael and Sarah were back from San Francisco, and Sarah had launched into a feverish round of entertaining to acquaint their Paris friends with current styles in America. Gertrude and Leo were on every guest list, even though Gertrude protested that she didn't want to waste time hearing the same stories over and over. "Nonsense," Sarah told her, "you know I add a different twist each time. Besides, the guests aren't the same. You never know when you might meet someone interesting."

"I have met everyone in Paris worth the effort," Gertrude retorted.

"Are you sure? Alice B. Toklas is here. You haven't met her."

"*Who* is Alice B. Toklas?"

"A young woman about your age, a great admirer of Matisse. We met her in San Francisco. She'd been keeping house there for her widowed father, who's a banker. But when Michael and I came along and began talking about Paris, she decided to come here as soon as she could afford to. Strangely enough, soon after, her wealthy grandfather died and left her a sizable inheritance."

"How providential!" Gertrude grunted.

"Gertrude, dear, don't be closed-minded. I'm having a tea for Alice and her traveling companion, Harriet Levy, tomorrow. You've already met Harriet once in San Francisco. Come see for yourself if you think Alice Toklas is worth the effort."

"Oh very well," Gertrude grumbled. "But I won't arrive until three because I don't lunch until one, and I can't eat again for at least two hours."

"Fine! Tomorrow at three."

Although Gertrude went to Sarah's tea with a great deal of unwillingness, after she met Miss Toklas, she heartily wished she had arranged to come earlier. Miss Toklas' alert mind appealed at once to Gertrude, as did her open admiration of Gertrude's ability to write.

When the two visitors rose to leave, Gertrude was quick to invite Miss Toklas for a walk the following week. Looking surprised but pleased, Alice accepted and agreed to be at 27 Rue de Fleurus the next Wednesday at one-thirty.

Gertrude was eating lunch on the day scheduled when a note arrived:

> Dear Miss Stein,
>
> Miss Levy and I are lunching at one of the open air restaurants at the Bois de Boulogne. Our meal is taking longer than expected. Please forgive the inconvenience if I am later than one-thirty.
>
> Yrs.,
> A. Toklas

Gertrude was angry. What kind of effrontery was this? Did Alice Toklas think Gertrude's time so dispensable that she could waste an afternoon waiting for someone to finish lunch? Just then the bell to the pavilion rang.

"I'll answer it," Gertrude shouted to Hélène.

Scowling, Gertrude threw open the door. On the steps stood Miss Toklas, smiling and expectant.

"How dare you be late?" Gertrude demanded.

"But, Miss Stein. . ." Alice stammered.

"When I make an appointment with someone, I expect him to be prompt. Come in and wait while I change into something fresh."

Guiding Alice to a chair in the dining room, Gertrude left abruptly, taking a conspicuously long time to get ready. When she returned, her mood had changed from dark displeasure to childlike anticipation. Laughing, she took Miss Toklas by the arm and led her out the door and down the street, chatting gaily and gossiping as if nothing had happened.

As they walked along, Gertrude pointed out students from the Sorbonne and explained how Alice could tell which schools they attended by the different colored ribbons they wore. She playfully helped some children roll hoops and smiled at the nurses with white starched caps who were tending them. She talked about books in general and books in translation and told Alice that although she knew both German and French, she never read anything that wasn't in English because it was too annoying. Finally they stopped at a pastry shop.

"Let's go in here," Gertrude said. "This is the best place on the Left Bank for an ice praline." While they ate, Alice again apologized for being late.

"It was nothing," Gertrude replied. "Next Saturday

evening you will come to 27 Rue de Fleurus for dinner and arrive promptly at six-thirty. Then I will forgive you. Bring Harriet, too, if she wishes to come. You will meet interesting people and see unusual paintings."

On Saturday evening, Alice, accompanied by Harriet, rang the bell to the pavilion a few minutes before six-thirty. "*Mes chères*," Gertrude greeted them warmly. "You are early. Good, I will give you a tour of the apartment." Taking them through the tiny hall with its umbrella stand and mirrors, she stopped first in the dining room. Alice and Harriet looked with interest at the books that lined the walls and the drawings by Picasso and Matisse that were tacked on the doors.

"Miss Toklas," Gertrude said, with a twinkle in her eye, "you look at the books as if you had never seen this room before, and yet you sat here for over thirty minutes only last Wednesday."

"Yes," Alice murmured, "I did sit here for at least that long, but I saw nothing."

"Why?" Harriet asked.

Gertrude laughed heartily before Alice could answer and directed them from the pavilion through an open passageway to the atelier. Here the walls from floor to ceiling were covered with paintings. Pieces of Renaissance furniture filled the room, crowding against each other and against the cast iron stove that Gertrude liked to sit next to. One large Renaissance table served as a desk for Gertrude. On it were stacks of notebooks, the kind ordinarily used by French children, with pictures of earthquakes and explorations on the covers. These contained Gertrude's writings.

Leo came into the atelier, and Gertrude introduced him. Leo, looking very scholarly with his receding hairline and long reddish beard, nodded briefly.

More guests began to arrive, and Gertrude left Alice and Harriet so she could act as hostess. As she greeted one group after another, she could see Leo explaining the pictures to Alice, who was gazing at them in amazement: Picasso's Harlequins, his portrait of Gertrude, Gauguins, Renoirs, Cézannes, Valloton's portrait of Gertrude, and Matisse's *La Femme au Chapeau.* Gertrude wondered if Alice liked them. At the moment she seemed more curious about the gas lights that hung over the pictures than the paintings themselves.

A loud knock sounded at the door of the atelier. "Dinner is ready to be served," Hélène announced.

Leo appeared at Gertrude's side. "Where are Picasso and Fernande?" he asked.

"I can't imagine. Picasso is always on time."

"Well, Picasso or no," Leo answered shortly, "Hélène will not wait."

From long experience, Gertrude knew this was true. Dinner was ready, and it must be eaten hot! Gertrude led everyone into the dining room, seated them, and nodded to Hélène that she should begin serving.

Just then a clatter could be heard in the courtyard outside, growing louder until Picasso and Fernande burst into the room. "I am so sorry," Picasso apologized at once. "You know, Gertrude, I am never late. I pride myself on having the punctuality of a king, but Fernande would not come until a new dress she had ordered was delivered. The dress was not delivered, and we are late, too. She has ruined our evening!" Fernande, beautiful as ever, was making her way to an empty chair, stopping to chat with friends as she went.

"No, Pablo," Gertrude laughed, "the evening is not

ruined. Come, sit here by Miss Toklas. You have missed nothing; Hélène has only started to serve."

Picasso sat down and, casting dark looks at Fernande, explained in fuller detail to everyone around him his woes with women. Then he calmed down and began eating with a good appetite and listening to the quiet talk of Alice Toklas. "I very much admire your portrait of Miss Stein," Gertrude heard Alice say.

"Yes," Picasso answered loud enough for Leo to hear, "everyone says she doesn't look like it, but that doesn't make any difference, she will."

The conversation around the table was lively, punctuated by loud cries of acclaim for Hélène's cooking. Gertrude liked the noise and excitement of these dinners, and she liked playing a key role in the lives of creative people. By entertaining as she and Leo did, she was assured a spot onstage. That was exactly where she wanted to be.

To Gertrude's surprise, soon after dinner Alice and Harriet said they must leave.

"So early! But why?"

"I am quite enervated," Harriet answered weakly, "I must go home and rest."

"Harriet underwent a religious conversion before we left San Francisco," Alice explained hastily. "It gave a kind of ecstasy to her life. But since our arrival in Paris, she says she has lost God and the strain of trying to find Him again is evidently very wearing."

"Why Harriet," Gertrude exclaimed, "what a dreadful state of mind! God hasn't deserted Paris."

"Oh please," Harriet said in a whisper, "don't blaspheme."

"Who's blaspheming? I live in Paris, and I've never lost God."

"But you are held by the Jewish faith and so is Alice."

"What difference does that make?"

"You have tradition to lean on."

Gertrude roared with laughter. "I'm afraid you don't know your history very well, Harriet, if you think tradition has ever saved a Jew. But don't be discouraged. If you really believe you have lost God and there is no hope you will ever find Him again, there is always an alternative."

"What's that?" Harriet asked, her eyes lighting up.

"You can kill yourself."

"Gertrude!" Alice gasped.

"I'm not being unkind, Alice. If Harriet thinks about it, the idea should be very comforting to her."

Harriet stared wild-eyed at Gertrude, then groaning lowly, she opened the door and disappeared into the night.

"What have you done?" Alice asked sternly.

"I gave her a sharp rap on the ego, which she sorely needed," Gertrude answered. "Harriet doesn't want to find God, she wants attention. Don't worry, Alice," Gertrude said, patting her on the arm, "Harriet's a smart girl. By tomorrow her condition will be much better—she may even be fully recovered." Gertrude linked her arm in Alice's and piloted her back to the after-dinner crowd that had now gathered in the atelier.

The next morning Gertrude was awakened by someone pounding on her bedroom door. "Mademoiselle Gertrude," Hélène called, "Miss Toklas is here to see you. She says it is a matter of great urgency."

Gertrude looked at the clock beside her bed. Ten o'clock. What could be urgent enough to get her out of bed so early? Didn't everyone know that she worked at night and slept in the morning? But since it was Alice. . .

"Tell Miss Toklas that I will be down shortly," she called to Hélène.

When Gertrude came downstairs, Alice was sitting with her back to the stairs, drinking coffee Hélène had brought. "Good morning, Alice."

"Oh Gertrude," Alice cried, jumping up from her chair, "Harriet sent me. She says she must see you at once."

"Before I have my coffee? Of course not. *Nothing* is that urgent."

"Then I'll go back and wait for you at the hotel," Alice said, starting for the door. "I mustn't leave Harriet long. I've been trying to dissuade her from suicide all night. This morning she was so exhausted she finally fell asleep, and I did, too. But within an hour she woke me to say she had seen God. She wanted to talk to you immediately."

"So," Gertrude laughed, pouring herself a cup of coffee. "Harriet would rather see God than kill herself. Do sit down, Alice," she suddenly commanded. "Harriet is not going to kill herself, and I'm not going to leave until I drink my coffee." Alice hesitated, but seeing that Gertrude wasn't going to budge, went back to her chair and sat down.

"Now that Harriet has seen God," Gertrude mused, "we must find someone else to take over her salvation. I think Sarah is the one. She's a Christian Scientist, a belief Harriet is temperamentally well suited for. Besides, Sarah and Harriet have been friends since they were children."

Gertrude's solution to the problem was a good one. Before long Sarah had convinced Harriet that if she read Mary Baker Eddy's *Science and Health* and if she practiced its teachings, she would find that life was worth living and that God was everywhere, even in Paris.

In the meantime Gertrude capitalized on Alice's free time by accepting her offer to help correct the proofs of *Three Lives*, which had just arrived from the Grafton Press. Gertrude was glad to have someone help with such exasperatingly detailed work and also to share her happiness that *Three Lives*, previously entitled *Three Histories*, was about to be published, even if at her own expense.

She had decided to publish the manuscript herself only after sending the manuscript to several publishers and invariably receiving the same reply: "Your work, Miss Stein, is too unusual for our company to gamble with." Gertrude consoled herself by believing that once *Three Lives* was in the hands of the public, she would never have to worry about publishing again.

After hours of exacting work, the proofs were corrected and sent to New York. No sooner was this task finished than Gertrude began struggling, entirely unsuccessfully, to type the beginning pages of her history of the Stein family, *The Making of Americans*.

"You are not suited for typing," Alice told her. "You have no aptitude for it."

"Yes, that is true," Gertrude sighed, "but it must be done. What am I to do?"

"You will finish writing the book. I will type the manuscript."

"No, that is impossible. You don't know how to type."

"I will teach myself."

Within a week Alice was typing accurately and with some speed. Gertrude was overjoyed. "How did you learn so quickly?" she asked.

"It is simple," Alice answered. "For years I have practiced Bach on the piano and know in what manner he organizes and what he emphasizes. The rhythm of your words is the same as the rhythm of a Bach fugue. I am well prepared to type them."

Throughout the winter of 1908, Gertrude enlisted Alice's help more and more frequently. Leo liked Alice and didn't object to her being at their apartment, but he thought she was assuming too much authority and seldom missed an opportunity to tell Gertrude so.

"Alice makes a fool of you, Gertrude. Why do you let her lead you around by the nose that way?"

"What do you mean?"

"You think she's working for you, but I hear how she scolds you and tells you what to do and I see that you do it!"

"You are wrong," Gertrude said, her dark eyes flashing hotly.

"No, I am not wrong. She manipulates you and makes you think you are dominating her. She is clever. You are stupid. As stupid about this as you are about your writing."

"Hélène!" Gertrude roared. "Bring my coat. I'm going out." At the door Gertrude turned to Leo, her face white with anger. "I am leaving because at this moment I dislike you so much that I cannot be reasonable. You are, of course, a bastard, and I think a day will come when you will very much regret having said these words to me." Leaving a dumbfounded Leo behind, she walked out the door.

eleven

"When I am old I wish to come back to Assisi and lead a black pig over the hills. I will put a red ribbon behind his ear."

Spring came and with it bright days and gentle fragrances that beckoned Gertrude into the air and sun. Every afternoon she strolled through the Luxembourg Gardens, happily aware as she walked under the pink and white blossoms of the chestnut trees how contented she was. Providence was smiling benignly on her: the writing of *The Making of Americans* was progressing well; her faith in herself, so dangerously threatened by Leo's disdain, had been restored by Alice Toklas' friendship; and most important of all, the tension between her and Leo had lessened to a point where they politely tolerated each other without open confrontations, a development that had taken place largely because Leo seldom stayed home. When he was there, he seemed abstracted and spent most of the time in his room.

After some months of this, Hélène anxiously inquired, "Why does Monsieur Leo go away so much?"

"He is in love, Hélène," Gertrude joked and laughed merrily.

"Oh Mademoiselle. Is Monsieur Leo really in love?"

"Well, I've heard rumors, Hélène. . ."

As summer drew near, Leo spent more time at 27 Rue de Fleurus. He and Gertrude talked of going to the Casa Ricci near Fiesole, Italy, again. Gertrude loved the Casa Ricci with its terraced hanging gardens, potted tubs of oranges, and breathtaking view of Florence and the Arno valley, but she hated to lose valuable working hours by moving away from Alice, who had become proficient in deciphering her handwriting and translating it into neat manuscript form. When Gertrude discussed her dilemma with Sarah, an easy solution became apparent.

Michael and Sarah had made plans to rent a larger villa in Fiesole, the Villa Bardi, for the summer. "You and Leo can stay with us," Sarah said, "and Alice and Harriet can rent the Casa Ricci." Alice and Harriet were enthusiastic about this suggestion. They wanted to see something of Italy, and this seemed the perfect opportunity. As for Leo, he was more than agreeable, glad to save money on rent so he could buy more paintings.

Gertrude's summer was full to the brim with writing, outings planned by Michael, Sarah, and Leo, and sight-seeing with Alice. "Come along with us," Gertrude always asked Harriet when she called for Alice. But Harriet inevitably declined, electing instead to study Christian Science alone or have a lesson with Sarah.

For touring, Gertrude and Alice rented the only car for hire in Fiesole, a dilapidated and disreputable taxicab, which in spite of its condition and its predilection for sputtering always arrived and returned. Glad for any form of transportation, the two women happily jounced over the Italian roads to Florence, Siena, and Rome.

When the cab could not be rented, they took pilgrimage walks in deference to a favorite of Gertrude's, Saint Francis. Once they climbed over difficult terrain to the spot where Saint Francis and Saint Dominic had met, and another time at high noon they made a pilgrimage walk from Perugia across the hot valley to Assisi. While crossing the valley, Gertrude, who thrived on walking in the hot sun, urged Alice to an ever faster pace. "We must pass these malodorous pilgrims," she insisted, "and arrive at Assisi in time to see the women leading their little black pigs over the hills."

"Gertrude, I *cannot* walk faster," Alice replied, her face streaked with dirt and tears of fatigue.

But Gertrude pretended not to hear and marched ahead even faster than before. Somehow Alice managed to keep up. By dusk the two friends were standing above the city of Assisi looking down upon the pilgrims winding their way up the purple hills. Their low chanting echoed over the valley.

"See there," Gertrude pointed to a woman with a black pig. "We have come to honor Saint Francis, and we have come to see this—an old woman with a black pig. When I am old, I wish to come back to Assisi and lead a black pig over the hills. I will put a red ribbon behind his ear."

Before the summer was over, Michael and Sarah returned to their Paris apartment, for they were considering another trip to San Francisco, and Michael wanted to confirm temporary business arrangements. Harriet went with them, and soon sent Alice a telegram saying that Michael and Sarah were ready to book passage to America and that she was going to return with them. What did Alice intend to do?

"You will stay in Paris," Gertrude said when Alice read the message aloud to her. "Why should you return to San Francisco?"

"My father is a lonely man; he needs me."

"Your father has his work and business associates. He doesn't need you. But I do! Who would type my manuscripts?"

"You could hire someone."

"I will *not* hire anyone. You said yourself that your fingers were adapted to the rhythm of my words. When we return to Paris, you will move your things to 27 Rue de Fleurus. I will work at night; you can type in the morning; and in the afternoon we can entertain ourselves as we please. I will inform Leo of this arrangement."

"Alice Toklas at 27 Rue de Fleurus!" Leo exclaimed when Gertrude told him. "I think she is hardly the type to live our kind of life. She strikes me as being very proper."

"She will learn!" Gertrude replied.

"Well," Leo said, scowling, "if you are asking for my permission, you have it. But I don't think either of you know what you're getting into."

"I know!"

"But does *she*?"

Back in Paris, Gertrude and Leo helped Alice move her belongings to 27 Rue de Fleurus. Although the quarters were crowded, Alice settled comfortably into the Steins' living schedule, doing her part by acting as secretary for Gertrude and using her superior culinary knowledge to help with the cooking.

Soon after their return, Picasso came to call on Gertrude. "You never come to see me when you return from anywhere," he complained. "Why is that so?"

"Ah, Picasso," Gertrude said, kissing him on both cheeks, "it is because I love you and want to savor the sweet expectancy of seeing you again."

"You are a beautiful liar, *ma* Gertrude."

"And you are a tragic Spaniard. Why do you come today with a face so long it touches your feet?"

"Because I am a failure. Yes, it is true, I am a failure."

"Why do you say this?"

"It is so! This morning I reviewed my past and was saddened by the way the critics dislike me. When I painted the Blue Period, they called my work grotesque, ugly; when I painted the Rose Period, they said I was too sweet; and now that I am influenced by African sculpture and I paint *Les Demoiselles d'Avignon* they call me mad."

"They are right! You *are* mad—for spending so much time thinking about critics. People do call your works ugly. I hear it all the time. But I see that your artist friends are imitating *Les Demoiselles d'Avignon* and I hear that the critics are still collecting your paintings. What more do you want—the whole world to fall at your feet? Now, have you nothing but a tragic face to show me? I have been away all summer, don't you know any gossip?"

Picasso shook his head. "You are cruel to me, Gertrude, just like all the rest."

"Yes, Pablo," Gertrude replied, laughing warmly, "and you love it. Now, tell me some gossip."

"I only know old gossip, such as Leo's love affair with Nina Auzias."

"Be serious, Pablo!"

"You do not know? Do you go about with a sack over

your head that you do not know about Leo and Nina Auzias?"

Gertrude looked smug. "Maybe I know, and maybe I don't. Tell me the story anyway, Pablo."

"The story is this," Pablo said, pulling his chair close to Gertrude so they were knee to knee, as was their habit when in serious conversation. "Nina Auzias is a nice-looking girl who models for various artists. Leo is one of them. She used to be a dancer but turned to modeling when she discovered how profitable it could be. She says that some years ago she was sitting under a chestnut tree in the Luxembourg Gardens when down the street straight toward her came the mate of her desires, a golden-bearded, graceful creature who looked like an Egyptian god. She was so enraptured that she cried out to some friends who were sitting with her, 'See that man who is passing? He will be my husband, I know it.' They laughed and called out, 'Mad girl! The mate of your desires is the great American, Leo Stein!' "

Gertrude hooted with laughter. "Nina Auzias is a clever girl. Leo would love anyone who told this story and called him 'the great American, Leo Stein.' "

"Yes," Picasso chuckled, "I thought the same."

"Does gossip say Leo will marry her?"

"No, he is too jealous of Nina Auzias' other lovers."

"Why does she have other lovers? I thought Leo was the mate of her desires."

"Yes, that is so, but she lives with other men, too, because it is profitable."

Gertrude was quiet for a minute and then she said, "It is good for me, Pablo, that this diversion came along for Leo. With him away so much my life is peaceful, and very full, too, since Alice Toklas moved in."

"Ah, and how does little Miss Toklas with her small feet and golden earrings like your way of life?"

"She hasn't seen much of it yet."

Picasso's eyes sparkled. "Then she must come to the banquet Fernande and I are giving in honor of Henri Rousseau. That is one reason I came this afternoon, to invite you and Leo and Miss Toklas."

Gertrude looked skeptical. "What are you up to, Pablo?"

"Nothing, nothing. We are giving the banquet to celebrate a painting by Rousseau I recently purchased for one dollar in a junk shop. It is a portrait of an old school mistress of his. I like it very much. Henri Rousseau should be praised for such a piece."

"I am not stupid, Pablo. I see what you intend. You are flaunting your approval of Rousseau in front of the academicians who have been so critical of your work."

"Gertrude, you wound me to think such a thing."

"Go home, Pablo," Gertrude laughed. "I love the wicked in you as well as the good. We will come to your banquet."

On the night of the banquet for Rousseau, the guests had been directed to assemble first at Fauvet's neighborhood cafe for apéritifs. When Gertrude, Leo, and Alice arrived, Marie Laurencin, a young French painter, was dancing about in a slow and lilting manner and wailing in low tones in anticipation of seeing her estranged lover, the poet Guillaume Apollinaire. Just as her wailing reached a crescendo, Fernande appeared in the doorway, greatly agitated. "The banquet will not be held," she cried, "because of the stupidity of the caterer. He has not brought the food, and his shop is now closed."

Alice Toklas, who had long been in charge of preparing

food in her father's house, rose to the emergency. "Come, Fernande," she said, "we will go to other shops and find the food you need."

While Alice and Fernande were gone, the guests began climbing the long hill to Picasso's apartment. Gertrude and Leo took charge of Marie Laurencin, struggling to keep her from falling down the hill as she alternately danced forward and feinted backward between them, accompanying herself by singing a song.

Before they were up the hill, Fernande and Alice hurried past, their arms loaded with bags of food. Fernande murmured something under her breath and cast dark looks at Marie Laurencin. When Gertrude and Leo and Marie Laurencin arrived at the door of Picasso's apartment, they found Fernande barring the way. "Marie Laurencin may not come in," she announced. "I will not have her ruining our lovely party. This is a serious party, a serious banquet for Rousseau, and neither I nor Pablo will tolerate such conduct."

"Stand aside, Fernande," Gertrude shouted, puffing heavily, "I'll be damned if I have struggled all the way up that terrific hill with Marie Laurencin only to be turned back. Besides, Rousseau and Apollinaire will be here soon, and it is imperative that we have everyone seated before they arrive. You do not want Marie Laurencin howling outside the door, do you?"

Picasso had by that time arrived from the back of the studio and said, "Yes, yes, Fernande, stand aside, let her in."

Grudgingly, Fernande stood back so Gertrude and Leo could deposit their burden in a chair. No sooner had they propped her in what they thought was a sitting position than she fell over into a plate of cherry tarts that had been placed near the chair. In exasperation, Gertrude left her there to go in search of Alice, who was helping prepare Fernande's specialty, *paella a la Valenciana*—chicken, fish, lobster, sausage, and pimiento in rice with artichokes and green peas.

Fernande had seated the guests, and Picasso was pouring the wine when Apollinaire ushered Rousseau into the room. There was a moment of silence in honor of the white-headed little man as he found his way to the seat of honor, but the silence was broken by the renewed wailing of Marie Laurencin when she was made aware that her lover had arrived. Apollinaire quickly took charge of her amid the general uproar and Fernande's shrieks of "She is ruining our lovely party. Throw her out. Throw her out!" Apollinaire soon quieted Marie Laurencin, and the banquet began in earnest.

Georges Braque, a disciple of Picasso's new style, cubism, played background music on his accordion, and Apollinaire read an ode he had composed about Rousseau's adventures in Mexico. "That is a very nice poem," Rousseau said when Apollinaire was finished, "but I have never been to Mexico."

"No?" responded Apollinaire. "Well if you had, you would have been as courageous as the ode says."

"A great disservice has been done Henri Rousseau!" André Salmon, the poet-journalist shouted, as he jumped up on the table. "Your poem, Apollinaire, does not recite his glory as it should." So saying, Salmon began praising the greatness of Rousseau on such a scale that he worked himself into a kind of spasm and had to be lifted off the table and deposited in a lower apartment with the guests' coats.

By this time wine and old age had quite overcome the

guest of honor. After whispering to Picasso, "It is good, Pablo, that we are seated near each other, for we are both great painters—myself in the modern style, and you in the Egyptian," he fell asleep amid so much commotion that not until hours later did anyone realize that a candle from a Chinese lantern was dripping wax on his head. By three o'clock in the morning, when the party broke up, he had a cap of wax so high he could hardly lift his head.

After the Steins had taken charge of Rousseau and seen him home, Gertrude asked Alice, who was *very* quiet, what she thought of the evening.

"I thought it amusing."

"Is that all? You just thought it amusing?"

"Yes," Alice answered, grim-faced, "that is all!"

Gertrude Stein in her studio, about 1905

Leo, Gertrude and Michael at 27 rue de Fleurus, about 1907

Gertrude's writing table and studio at 27 rue de Fleurus

Gertrude Stein at her desk at 27 rue de Fleurus, about 1923

Old postcard showing Gertrude Stein and Alice B. Toklas at the birthplace of Marshall Joffre, Rivesaltes, France, April 1917 (driving a truck for American Friends of French Wounded)

Picasso, Gertrude Stein, Madame Georges Maratier and Alice B. Toklas on the terrace at Bilignin, 1930

Gertrude Stein, Madame Olga Picasso, Picasso at Bilignin, 1930

Gertrude Stein and Alice B. Toklas, Bilignin, June 1934 (photograph by Carl Van Vechten)

Gertrude Stein and Virgil Thomson

Gertrude Stein and a neighboring farmer, Monsieur Lambert, with his two children, Bilignin, 1939

Gertrude Stein, Bilignin, 1939

Gertrude Stein, Alice B. Toklas, Basket II, and some American soldiers, 5 rue Christine, 1946

Gertrude Stein at 5 rue Christine, 1946 (photograph by Andre Ostier)

twelve

"The days are wonderful and the nights are wonderful and the life is pleasant."

Early one morning in the spring of 1912, Gertrude put her pen down on the Renaissance table that she used for a desk in the atelier and went into the pavilion. "Get out your Spanish *mantilla*," she called up the stairs to Alice's bedroom. "I've just finished *The Making of Americans* and we're going to Spain to celebrate."

In spite of the early hour, Alice's firm, deep voice shot back immediately, "I don't want to go to Spain. I would hate the bullfights."

"Nonsense! You will love the bullfights. Get dressed and come down at once."

As Gertrude sat in the dining room waiting for Alice, she thought of her long struggle to complete *The Making of Americans*, now an opus of well over a thousand pages. For five years she had hovered over it nightly like a great maternal bird, struggling with its heavy and sometimes awkward proportions. She had seen its breadth from the beginning, however, and had held true to the course she had originally designed.

There was something Biblical about this work. She knew it, and Alice did, too. But would publishers? *Three Lives* had not sold well, in spite of encouraging remarks from friends, who said that she was creating a new genre in literature. Most people thought her work strange and were outspoken about telling her so. Bernard Berenson said, "Your prose beats me hollow and makes me dizzy to boot."

Far from being discouraged by such remarks, Gertrude was more determined than ever to get her writing into the hands of the public, where she believed she would be understood. After all, *The Making of Americans* was written in the language of the common people whose history, like the Stein family's, was a history of repeating, ever repeating, until they *created* something in their lives.

Alice's voice broke into Gertrude's thinking. "*Must* we go to Spain?" she asked.

"Of course we must. With one piece of writing done, I need inspiration for another. And Spain is the place to go. When Leo and I toured Spain in 1903, I fell in love with the simple joy and tragedy of the landscape. This is what I want to see again, simple joy and simple tragedy."

Alice succumbed and began to pack.

On the day of their departure, Mildred Aldrich, an author friend, came to the station to see them off. "Have a marvelous time, and write!" she called as the train began to move.

"Look for a publisher for me while I'm gone," Gertrude called back. But Mildred's answer was lost in the loud wail of the train's whistle.

"Now," Alice said, settling back in her seat, "may I see the schedule?"

Gertrude had carefully mapped out their trip to Spain but had refused to let Alice see the route before they left. "If I let you see it before we are on the train," she had said, "you will make reservations at all the spots I have marked. Then how can I change my mind at the last minute, which you know I am bound to do."

Alice had argued that to make reservations was wise and that they would enjoy their trip more if they could anticipate where they were going and when they would arrive. But Gertrude would not give in. To her the greatest pleasure in traveling was the adventure of unknowing, and this she intended to have.

Now, with the train wheels moving rapidly under her, Gertrude felt safe in showing Alice the itinerary. Alice scanned the list of cities and approximate staying time. "Only two days in Avila!" she exclaimed. "But that is the birthplace of Saint Theresa. Surely we can stay longer than two days."

"Two days!" Gertrude said firmly, reclaiming her schedule. "Unless, of course," she added with a twinkle in her eye, "*I* find a reason to stay longer."

At Burgos, their first stop, they toured a beautiful Gothic cathedral and then turned south to Valladolid and on to Avila. As they drew near to Avila in the late afternoon, they had a breathtaking view of St. Theresa's cathedral. They stepped from the train into a waiting coach pulled by four mules with bells on their harnesses. The bells joggled and so did Gertrude and Alice as they rode to the inn along the cobbled roads. "Do you still want to stay more than two days?" Gertrude shouted above the clatter. Alice nodded her head as properly as she could under the circumstances. Gertrude roared with laughter.

They stayed in Avila for two weeks, enraptured by everything they saw, but especially by St. Theresa's church and by a chapel completely covered in beaten gold and decorated with coral ornaments that had been sent from America in the seventeenth century.

From Avila they went to Madrid, where Gertrude acquired seats for the bullfight in a shady spot on the first row under the President's box. She told Alice when to look and when not to look so she would see all the beauty and grace of the toreadors and none of the injuries to the animals. When a horse was being gored, she said, "Do not look." And when the horse had been led away, she said, "Now you can look." Alice admitted that she liked the fight very much, but if given a choice would rather look at cathedrals.

After leaving Madrid, they went to Toledo and then to the Escorial, where Gertrude could not look enough at the unusually somber landscape and architecture and where they saw a beautiful El Greco, *The Conversion of Saint Maurice*. From the Escorial they proceeded to Cuenca. There Gertrude wrote amusingly to Mildred Aldrich:

> Having attended the bullfight in Madrid with great success, we have now come as far as Cuenca, a lovely spot, and also the setting for a story about me which I think Alice will frequently find opportunity to tell, so I suppose I better tell it on myself first.
>
> We arrived for lodgings in Cuenca at night, and were told that the hotel was set on a precip-

itous mountain and that directly below it was 'a sudden and deep descent that dropped into a wild torrent in the valley below.' As you know, I am terrified of heights, so after we ate a large dinner of wild game and had gone to our room to prepare for bed, I insisted that we close both windows, for I was afraid that in the night I would walk in my sleep and fall out the window into 'the wild torrent below.' Alice finally consented, but not without mentioning that we would be uncomfortable sleeping without air. She was right. I hardly slept a wink. The next morning when we arose, grumpy from lack of sleep, Alice discovered that our room was against the mountain—the rooms on the other side of the hotel dropped to the sudden and deep descent. Well, anyway, that's the way it happened. Alice now uses this story as an example of how I exaggerate my fears.

Spain is as tragic and gay as I remember. Its starkness inspires me. I feel an urge to capture the *whole* of my impressions, to form a visual and sensual experience through words. I have been trying to describe rooms with this in mind, and I'm quite excited about the results. So is Alice. We call my attempts, *Tender Buttons*.

Also, I feel absolutely pontifical. As we travel, me in my usual brown garb, many peasants have mistaken me for a high church authority. Once when I was taking a walk, a group followed me and when I sat down they wanted to kiss my ring, thinking I was a bishop whom they were

> expecting to arrive in the town. I love the attention. Alice thinks I'm sacrilegious.
>
> Gertrude Stein

Because Gertrude had become very ill from a severe attack of indigestion and Alice was suffering from the heat, they cut short the last half of their trip and went right to Granada. When Gertrude felt the charm of this city, she quite forgot her illness.

The Dancing Gypsies of Granada especially fascinated her, with their whirling costumes and the rhythm of their lively feet. As she watched them day after day, she began to feel a new conviction—a desire to recreate in words the rhythm not only of the dance, but of the whole visible world. Under this mood she wrote three short pieces, *Susie Asado*, *Preciosilla*, and *Gypsies in Spain*.

At night in their room at the Washington Irving Hotel, Gertrude read her latest manuscripts aloud to Alice. From *Susie Asado* she read:

> A pot. A pot is a beginning of a rare
> bit of trees. Trees tremble, the old
> vats are in bobbles, bobbles which shade
> and shove and render clean. . .

"You are writing as the cubists paint," Alice commented.

"What do you mean?"

"You are using the same technique as Picasso. He braces his impressions against the rigid lines of Spanish architecture. You use the rigidity of words for the same purpose."

When the sun was too hot for Alice, Gertrude walked through the town alone, watching the swallows fly and bathing in the soft fragrance of myrtle and oleander. She loved to feel the hot sun burn into her face. Occasionally she stopped in a shop and bought a small figurine for herself or a piece of Spanish jewelry for Alice. All too soon it was time to return to Paris.

The first thing that greeted them upon their arrival home was a stack of telegrams from Mabel Dodge, an American heiress famous for her salon gatherings. Every telegram read the same:

> You promised to visit me in Florence when you returned from Spain. The Villa Curonia awaits you!

The second thing to greet them was the news that Leo had packed his belongings and left.

"But Hélène," Gertrude sputtered, dumbfounded by this development, "where has he gone?"

"To Florence, Mademoiselle."

"You mean he isn't ever coming back?"

"He said someday he would return for his share of the paintings. Over there, on the shelf, he left an address for you and a letter."

"Did he take Nina Auzias with him?"

"No."

Gertrude took the letter from the shelf and went into the atelier. All around her were pictures that she and Leo had purchased, representing a kind of history of their life together in Paris, a reminder of the best times and the worst.

She sat down at the Renaissance table and tore open the letter. In brief, Leo suggested that the Cézannes be divided equally between them, with the exception of the Cézanne *Apples*, which was uniquely important to him. He would make a clean sweep of the Renoirs, he said, and he urged Gertrude to do likewise with the Picassos. Above all things he wanted to be fair, and he hoped they would both live happily ever after while sucking gleefully their respective oranges.

Gertrude threw the letter down on the table. Leo! Always wanting the last word. Well, he could have it! She and Alice were going to the Villa Curonia. Leo could return from Florence and take what he wanted while they were gone. She would have Hélène write him to that effect.

When Gertrude announced her plans to Alice, Alice agreed, but added, "You must tell Michael and Sarah about Leo's moving before we go."

"No. If Leo hasn't told them himself, the Paris grapevine is absolutely dependable for that kind of thing. Besides, I have little in common with Michael and Sarah anymore. They promote Matisse; I promote Picasso."

"Don't alienate yourself from Michael and Sarah because you're angry with Leo, Gertrude."

"I said nothing about alienating. I simply said we have very little in common. And I prefer to keep it that way."

At the Villa Curonia, Gertrude found it easier than she imagined to forget Leo. Mabel Dodge was a stimulating and thoughtful hostess, and no inconvenience was too great if it added to the comfort of her guests, especially one she admired as much as Gertrude. Gertrude's favorite foods were served, a special room was set up for her to write and study in, and always Mabel tried to anticipate and provide for any of Gertrude's needs. Alice looked on with growing annoyance. She had grown accustomed to caring for Gertrude, and she didn't like having her position usurped.

Before many days had passed, Mabel was distracted from her adulation of Gertrude, for another guest was due to arrive, Constance Fletcher. "She comes frequently to the Villa Curonia," Mabel told Gertrude. "She wrote *Kismet* when she was only eighteen, you know."

Yes, Gertrude did know, and she also knew the legend that had grown up around Constance. After being jilted by Lord Lovelace, who was a descendant of Byron, she had gone to live with her stepfather, a pitiful man who had nearly gone insane following the death of Constance's mother. Every morning the two of them followed an elaborate ritual of strewing rose petals on the stairway where the dead woman had customarily walked. Gertrude loved such tales. She was curious to meet Constance Fletcher.

When the time drew near for Constance to arrive, Alice was dispatched to meet her at the station. She returned accompanied by a rather large, near-sighted woman dressed in vivid green. Gertrude could see that Alice was already under the spell of Miss Fletcher's charm. She herself soon followed suit.

"Mabel, dear," Constance said after the appropriate niceties were exchanged, "how are the ghosts?"

Gertrude looked up sharply. Was she serious?

"Quite well, I think," Mabel replied as evenly as if she were discussing a neighbor.

"Have you any new ones?"

"No, but your favorite is still here. She'll be delighted you are back."

"Ah, such a wistful ghost," Constance sighed, staring

into space for a moment. Then she turned to Gertrude and Alice, "She was an English governess. Killed herself."

"How terrible!" Alice exclaimed.

"Well, yes and no." Constance smiled.

After Miss Fletcher had retired for the night, Gertrude cornered Mabel. "Do you think it wise to encourage her hallucinations?"

"What hallucinations?"

"About ghosts."

"But we really have ghosts," Mabel replied sweetly on her way up the stairs.

Turning to go into her study room, Gertrude stopped when she heard Alice's voice upstairs in Constance Fletcher's room. "Goodnight, Miss Fletcher. Pleasant dreams."

"Thank you. I'm sure my night will be most entertaining," Constance's voice floated down the stairs. "My ghost friend will be here soon, and we will have a nice chat. Maybe she has already arrived. Sometimes she hides in that lovely old cupboard. Will you please open the door, Alice, and see if she is there?"

Gertrude could hear Alice crossing the room and opening a door.

"There you are, you naughty ghost!" Constance cried out. "You come right out of that cupboard and sit beside me on the bed. I have lots to tell you. Oh Alice, will you please close the door on your way out? I would hate to disturb the others with our chatter."

"What did you see in the cupboard?" Gertrude whispered when Alice came downstairs.

Alice's eyes were very large. "Nothing!" she answered shortly.

"But Constance Fletcher was talking to someone."

"I saw *nothing.*"

"Goodnight, Constance," Mabel called, but there was no answer. Only a faint murmur could be heard, punctuated occasionally with a refined girlish laugh. "Goodnight, Gertrude. Goodnight, Alice," Mabel called from the top of the stairs. "Don't be frightened by our ghosts. They're harmless."

"Harmless or not, I'm sleeping on the couch beside your desk," Alice muttered, and marched off to get linens and blankets.

Gertrude went to her desk. For a few minutes she sat thinking, and then across the top of a fresh sheet of paper she wrote, *Portrait of Mabel Dodge.* Underneath it, slowly, thoughtfully, she began, "The days are wonderful and the nights are wonderful and the life is pleasant."

thirteen

". . . once a thing is done,
it loses its appeal, you know."

Paris in the fall of 1912 was in holiday mood. Young artists from all over the world flocked there, hoping to catch a spark of the genius that had inspired cubism. A kind of breathless expectancy tingled in the air. On the sidewalks young men sat behind easels painting strong lines in bright colors. When Gertrude took her afternoon walks, she looked at the young men and their paintings and was thrilled with their confidence and hope. She loved movement and she loved change and certainly she loved the spirit of Paris in those exciting days.

"It's a renaissance!" Picasso proclaimed.

"No, Pablo," Gertrude countered, "it is only life as I have been telling you all these years it should be. Every day is a renewal, every morning the daily miracle. This joy you feel is *life*."

One of the young painters whom Gertrude especially admired was a Spaniard, Juan Gris. "He is the great one!"

Gertrude told Picasso. "He feels the mysticism that your painting lacks."

"*I* am the great one!" Picasso shouted, pounding his fists against his breast.

"No," Gertrude said sternly, "you were the first, Pablo, but Juan Gris is the great one."

Partially because of the new mood in Paris and partially because of Leo's absence, and the absence of the Renoirs and other paintings he had eventually taken, the character of Saturday evenings at 27 Rue de Fleurus changed. The crowds were less diligent in intellectual pursuits, freer to express experimental ideas. Gertrude, now the complete mistress of her household, reigned superbly over these gatherings. Drawing people close with the magnetism of her voice and her hearty good humor, she could hold them under her spell for hours. On the other hand, she could, if offended or undesirably contradicted, dismiss a person permanently with one icy statement.

Among those who came to the Saturday evenings were Henry McBride, Roger Fry, Wyndham Lewis, the infanta Eulalia, and a princess from Roumania. But the person who was to play the most important role in Gertrude's future was Myra Edgerly, a tall beautiful lady from San Francisco who had gained an extraordinary reputation in London as a miniaturist of royalty. She had heard about Gertrude's strange style of writing and was curious to know more about it.

"Please read something to me," she asked after she and Gertrude had talked for a while. "Something you especially like."

Gertrude read from her compilation of impressions called *Tender Buttons:*

> A feather is trimmed, it is trimmed by the light and the bug and the post, it is trimmed by little leaning and by all sorts of mounted reserves and loud volumes. It is surely cohesive.

Myra Edgerly stared at Gertrude blankly. "Please read it again," she said. Gertrude complied. When Gertrude finished a second time, Myra Edgerly smiled. "I like it," she said, "but it scares me a little because I don't know how I like it. I want to say, 'Yes, yes, that's it, that's a feather,' but I don't know *how* it's a feather—I don't know what you've done."

"Of course, that's the whole point."

"What's the whole point?"

"*That!*"

"Oh."

Myra Edgerly was quiet for a moment, then she said, "I know a publisher in England, John Lane, who is interested in experimental literature. I think he would like to have some of your work. Would you object if I wrote to him about you?"

"No," Gertrude replied half-heartedly, "but don't be surprised if he doesn't reply. I've been trying for five years to get my manuscripts published, with no luck so far."

"You mean you haven't published *anything?*"

"Only *Three Lives*, and that at my own expense."

"I will write John Lane today."

Before long a letter came to Gertrude from Mr. Lane. He would like to see her, he said, if she could come to England in January and attend one of his Sunday afternoon salons.

Gertude put the letter aside. "Well, that settles that."

"What do you mean?" Alice asked.

"I mean we can't go to England. I still have nightmares about the melancholy I suffered there."

"Gertrude," Alice said firmly, "if there is the slightest chance that this man will publish one of your books, I think we should go."

"I won't go, Alice."

"Gertrude, *I think we should go!*"

"Oh very well," Gertrude said crossly, "but we will have a perfectly miserable time."

When Gertrude and Alice arrived in England, the countryside was covered with a fresh blanket of snow. Soft mounds of white tempered the cold stiffness of winter, turning it into an idyllic landscape. "Why, England is beautiful!" Alice exclaimed when they stepped from the train.

"The countryside is beautiful," Gertrude muttered, "but London is *not* beautiful."

Myra Edgerly had arranged for Gertrude and Alice to stay with some friends of hers who lived outside the city before they traveled on to London. "You will need time to rest," she had told them, "and Colonel and Mrs. Rogers' country home is just the place. They will love having you, and you will love being there."

Gertrude did love being there. She basked in the comforts provided by her host and hostess. Only one thing disturbed her: the sound of the human voice forever speaking English. "It drives me to distraction," she complained to Alice. "If English is to be spoken in unbroken intervals, I want it to be my voice. I could never live here. No, I could never live anywhere but in Paris. The French language is soothing. English is harsh."

After leaving the Rogers', Gertrude and Alice accepted Roger Fry's invitation to stay with him a few days at his country home just outside London. Roger Fry was an enigma to most of his friends, but Gertrude thought of him as a kindred soul and admired his progressive ideas. Behind him was a brilliant career as director of the Metropolitan Museum of Art and art adviser to J. P. Morgan. He had astonished the art world by relinquishing these positions to take up the cause of the Postimpressionists. In London he was currently giving his support to the Bloomsbury group, a group that Gertrude chose to refer to as "The Young Men's Christian Society—with Christ left out." At Roger Fry's Gertrude learned that John Lane's wife had read *Three Lives* and liked it so much she was encouraging her husband to publish it.

The next Sunday afternoon Gertrude and Alice went to the Lanes' salon. Mr. Lane was very personable and kind, but he did not talk about Gertrude's writing. "Please come back next Sunday," he said at the end of the afternoon. The next week Gertrude and Alice returned. "Frankly, Miss Stein," Mr. Lane said, "I would like to publish your work, but at the present time my finances are uncertain. I will be in Paris soon and will be in touch with you then." With only this weak promise, Gertrude was forced to acknowledge that her business in England was over, and with results much less fruitful than she had hoped. Heavyhearted, the two friends left for home.

Gertrude was saved from complete discouragement by letters that began arriving from Mabel Dodge. She was in New York attending the Armory Show where many Paris artists were having their first American showing. Through a series of unlikely circumstances, Miss Dodge had been asked to write a review of Gertrude's work, relating it to the new art movement. She chose her favorite piece, *Portrait of Mabel Dodge at the Villa Curonia*, and did such a fine job on her unexpected assignment that she not only assured Gertrude's fame, but her own as well. She wrote to Gertrude:

> You are on the eve of bursting. Everybody wherever I go—& others who go where I don't say the same thing—is talking of Gertrude Stein.

"Wonderful!" Gertrude purred when she read Mabel's enthusiastic account. "Don't you think so, Alice?"

"I think," said Alice, vehemently, "that Mabel Dodge is enjoying a great deal of undeserved fame."

"Oh Alice, you're jealous."

"Yes, and you should be, too. She is assuming the glory that belongs to you!"

Gertrude frowned and put the letter down. It *did* seem that Mabel's exuberance was self-centered. Gertrude's next letter to Mabel was unfriendly and businesslike. "If I'm achieving some fame," she thought, "*I* will take the bows. *No* one is going to stand proxy for Gertrude Stein!"

Suddenly rumors of national unrest and even of war broke into Gertrude's thinking. She had heard them on the periphery of her activities but had kept them at bay by concentrating on developing her own fame. Now that her trip to England was over, she found the rumors increasingly difficult to ignore.

She tried to shut them out by working on short portraits, similar to the one she had done of Mabel Dodge. One of these was of Carl Van Vechten, music critic for

The New York Times, who had captured the affections of both Gertrude and Alice.

But that spring new friendships and portrait-writing were not diversion enough, for along with the threat of war came another unwelcomed sound: an inner voice whispering that Saturday nights were not as interesting as they used to be. Was her old exciting life passing away? Although only forty, Gertrude sometimes felt very old. She needed an activity to make her forget the dark mood that was pressing increasingly heavy upon her.

Remodeling 27 Rue de Fleurus was the answer, she decided. Alice agreed, and they began. A passageway was built between the studio and the atelier, and electricity was installed in their living quarters. They had just finished wallpapering when a message arrived from John Lane announcing he would call on them the following day. "But he cannot!" Alice cried. "We can't possibly be ready to receive him."

"Of course you will," Gertrude calmly replied. And with the greatest faith that Alice and Hélène would have everything in order, she retired to the atelier.

When John Lane arrived, 27 Rue de Fleurus was ready for him. Alice, gracious and unruffled, met him at the door, giving no sign that only fifteen minutes earlier she had placed the last piece of furniture and dashed to the bedroom to don her favorite dress and long golden earrings. Gertrude peacefully greeted their caller from her chair by the iron stove in the atelier.

Mr. Lane's visit was brief and pointed. "I have just about decided to publish *Three Lives,*" he said. "But I would like you to come to London so we can agree on details."

"I am in favor of your publishing *The Making of Americans*, Mr. Lane."

"No, I have heard about *The Making of Americans*. It is too long."

"Would you consider doing a collection of all the portraits I have written up to this time?"

"I would consider it."

"Then we will come to London."

"Fine," John Lane replied, rising to go, "July will be convenient."

On July 5, Gertrude and Alice alighted at the Victoria Station in London. Although the threat of war thundered ever louder, Gertrude tried hard to ignore it. The very *thought* of war terrified her. She was relieved to find that at John Lane's regular salon gathering, the guests seemed no more than superficially interested in world affairs. War was only one of many subjects being tossed about.

Mr. Lane was eager to discuss business with Gertrude. "I have decided," he said, "to publish *Three Lives* and nothing more. If *Three Lives* proves profitable to both of us, I would consider contracting for more of your work."

"You are firmly against publishing the portraits?"

"Yes, until you are better known."

Gertrude considered for a moment. "Very well," she said abruptly. "Let's start working on a contract."

Sunday afternoon turned into evening and still they had not agreed on all matters. "I cannot stay longer," Gertrude said at last. "We will have to postpone the signing date."

"Good. I need time to think over the questions you've posed anyway."

"I must have a contract within two weeks," Gertrude warned.

"You will have a contract within two weeks, Miss Stein."

With such a promise made, Gertrude's spirits soared. At last she had a publisher for something. "We will go to the theater; we will shop for new furniture; we will accept invitations!" she told Alice excitedly. And all these things they did, inebriated by the happy mood of Gertrude's success.

Invitations flooded in. One, to meet Henry James, was sent by the photographer Alvin Coburn. However, to both Gertrude's and Alice's disappointment, on the day appointed, Henry James was ill and the arrangements had to be canceled. But this bad luck was more than compensated for when at a dinner party in Cambridge they were introduced to Alfred North Whitehead and his wife. Before parting that evening, the Whiteheads invited Gertrude and Alice to spend the next weekend with them. "We would be delighted," Gertrude quickly responded. Already she admired Whitehead's dignified and scholarly manner.

Returning to London the next day, Gertrude worked out the dissenting points with John Lane and the contract was signed. "Are you pleased?" Alice asked when Gertrude returned to their hotel room with the contract in her pocket.

"Yes, though once a thing is done, it loses its appeal, you know. Now I'm more excited about a weekend with the Whiteheads." In high spirits they boarded the train to Salisbury Plain, expecting to leave for Paris when the weekend was over.

fourteen

"Nothing is certain in war."

"War! No, no, no, I will *not* have it!" Gertrude said, stomping her foot.

"But you must have it. It has been declared," Alice answered. She was trembling, badly shaken by the news.

"Well, I don't want to hear about it. Don't talk about it any more."

"Gertrude, be reasonable. We are guests of the Whiteheads. War has been declared. It will be discussed. You cannot avoid it."

"I *will* avoid it. We will leave for Paris."

"We can't. I have already checked. No one is allowed out of the country."

"Tell them Gertrude Stein is leaving for Paris!"

"Gertrude, please."

Quite beside herself with grief and fear, Gertrude began pulling clothes from the drawers and stuffing them into bags. "Gertrude, calm yourself!" Alice quietly ordered.

With tears streaming down her face, Gertrude turned to her friend. "Oh Alice, please say there is no war."

Unable to cope with such a childlike plea from her friend whom she loved so well, Alice burst into tears and fell into Gertrude's arms. The two women clung to each other, trying in vain to block out the ugly truth.

"We were so happy," Gertrude murmured. "27 Rue de Fleurus newly redecorated, a contract with a publisher signed, stimulating friends–and now this . . . now bombings, and killings, and never knowing whether one should wish to be dead or alive. Oh Alice, it's cruel!"

"No, Gertrude," Alice said, wiping her eyes, "it won't be cruel unless we weaken."

"Gertrude–Alice!" Mrs. Whitehead called, rapping on the door.

Fortified by Alice's strength, Gertrude went to the door and opened it.

"England at war! It's unbelievable!" Mrs. Whitehead cried, fluttering into the room. "You must not think of moving a step from this house. Traveling will be frightfully dangerous, if not impossible. We have plenty of room. You must stay."

Gertrude and Alice did stay, and were very appreciative of the Whiteheads' kindness. They made a hurried trip to London to collect their trunks and to cable relatives in America for money, and then they returned to the safety of Lockridge.

Yet even in the country, danger sometimes seemed alarmingly near. Gertrude was terrified. Alfred North Whitehead suggested that she divert her attention by joining him in his daily walks about the English countryside. Gertrude gratefully accepted his invitation. For hours on end they walked, talking of history and philosophy. All around them autumn colors blazed brightly. The weather was exceptionally fine. How good life could be without war, Gertrude thought.

But the war bulletins grew progressively worse. The Germans were approaching Paris. "I hate to mention this," Mr. Whitehead said, "but are all your manuscripts in Paris?"

"Yes," Gertrude answered, and retired to her room. She couldn't bear to hear war discussed any longer. When Alice came to call her for dinner, Gertrude was lying on the bed, her face turned to the wall.

"Gertrude, are you ill?"

"No, I am mourning for Paris."

"But Paris still stands."

"It won't for long."

"You don't know that. You're being childish again. Now come, eat your dinner. It's rude to keep the Whiteheads waiting."

"No, I am not coming, nor am I leaving this room until I hear that Paris is safe."

Numb with grief, Gertrude could neither think nor act logically. For days she stayed in her room, mourning. Manuscripts were not important, nor were pictures. But Paris . . .

Then one day, breathless with excitement, Alice rushed into Gertrude's room. "Paris is saved! The Germans have been turned back."

Gertrude looked at her blankly, unbelieving. "Don't tell me such things."

"But it's true, I tell you, it is *true*."

"You are sure?"

"Yes, I am sure."

Tears of relief and joy rolled down Gertrude's cheeks.

Since Paris had not fallen to the Germans, Gertrude gained confidence about the war and about herself. She emerged from her room eager for political discussions and full of plans for leaving. Every day her courage grew. Not even the endless delays in acquiring traveling papers dampened her enthusiasm. Finally, on October 15, she and Alice left for Paris.

Their trip was exhausting. They crossed the channel in a crowded boat and saw for the first time the tired, watchful eyes of soldiers. Then they boarded a train for Paris, and late that night found a taxi to take them home. Home! Cold, dark, with very little food in the pantry; nevertheless, Gertrude thought, nothing had ever looked so good to her before.

When they first returned, Gertrude was determined to live an orderly life. "War or no war, we will live according to a schedule. We will eat when it is time to eat. We will sleep when it is time to sleep. And certainly I will work when it is time to work." Being home seemed to give her the strength she needed to fight her fears.

After the first Zeppelin alarm, though, Gertrude saw that an inflexible life was out of the question. Alice had retired early that night, and Gertrude had started her usual routine of writing until sunup. She was deep in thought when the Zeppelin alarm sounded. At first she couldn't identify it. When its howling persisted, the message of danger it signaled sent terror flashing into her brain. "Be calm!" she ordered herself. She must *not* give in to fear again as she had at the Whiteheads'.

Resolutely she went to the bottom of the stairs and called gently, "You'd better get up, Alice. Put on something warm and come downstairs."

Because their French friends were always talking about

some kind of revolution, Alice was more fearful of this than an enemy attack. Being awakened so abruptly, she naturally cried out, "What is it? Oh Gertrude, is it a revolution?"

"No, I don't think so. But you had better come down anyway." Fearful that Alice would turn on a light, Gertrude went up the stairs to meet her. "Here, give me your hand, I will guide you."

Downstairs, she settled Alice on the couch and went in search of blankets. When she returned, Alice was sitting up, huddling over her knees. "You have heard it said that a person's knees knock when he is afraid? Well, I didn't believe it until now. But mine would be making a terrible clatter if I weren't holding them together."

Gertrude covered Alice with a warm shawl. They sat together in the dark and listened to a loud boom and several weaker ones. For a time it was quiet, and then horns began blowing. Gertrude got up and turned on the lights.

"Is it over?" Alice asked.

"Yes, for now it is over."

The entire winter was cold and uncertain. Cold because there wasn't enough coal to heat even one small room, and uncertain because, as Gertrude sadly admitted, "Nothing is certain in war."

One day a letter came from Donald Evans, a publisher in New York. Through the suggestion of Carl Van Vechten, he was writing Gertrude to ask if she would let him publish the manuscript she had written in Spain called *Tender Buttons*. He understood that she had described objects, rooms, and food in a most unusual way. His firm was known as Claire Marie, and he would like to send her a contract.

Gertrude's interest was only slightly aroused. "What strikes me," she said, "is not that at last someone wants to publish my writing, but that such an ordinary business venture should be suggested when we do not know if to-morrow we will even be alive." But as she prepared the manuscript to be sent, Gertrude was glad to have her mind diverted from war to publishing, even for a little while.

Slowly the winter dragged on. A few friends dropped in. Picasso came with Eve, who had replaced Fernande, and occasionally Gertrude saw Juan Gris. Mildred Aldrich came and told of watching the Battle of the Marne, fought just below her house. Comforting as these friends were, in the spring Gertrude decided they must get away from the war for a while. They went back to Spain, to the little town of Terreno just outside Palma de Mallorca.

Here they found a small house, and with their French servant, Jeanne, whom they hired after Hélène left in the fall, they settled comfortably into the easy rhythm of the community. Gertrude liked the peaceful gentle hills and warm evenings. Alice liked the garden that grew abundant crops of fruits, vegetables, and nuts.

The countryside inspired Gertrude to write plays. Plot, she concluded, was unimportant. What she wanted was to convince her audience that drama as a genre was compelled by ritual and beauty of movement. Every day she took a walk, basking in the harmony of hills, fields, sky, and climate. When she returned home to write, her impressions flew lightly through her pen. Sometimes she quite lost herself to the ballet of movement she was creating.

Life in Spain was peaceful, and Gertrude's interest in playwriting absorbed her attention most of the time, but the shadow of war still hovered over her. One reminder she grew to loathe. Each time the Germans achieved a victory, a governess in a house close by gleefully unfurled the German flag and set it flying. "Damn it!" Gertrude exploded one day, starting for the door, "I'm going over there and tear that flag down."

"No, no," Alice interceded. "You will be arrested."

"Then what do you suggest?"

Alice thought a moment. "When the Allies are victorious, we will raise the tricolor." Gertrude's scowling face broke into a smile.

When the next Allied victory was announced, Gertrude rushed to get the tricolor. Attaching it to a strong cord, she hurled it high, letting it wave on a pole over the house. That night she read the memoirs of Queen Victoria, content in the belief that she was doing her part to win the war.

They stayed in Terreno through the winter and the following spring, and then considered going home. But news from Paris was still so depressing that they elected to stay another winter. By the second spring, reports were encouraging, and they felt they could safely return.

In contrast to the saddened city they had left over two years before, Paris was optimistic when they arrived. Everywhere people were participating in the war movement. Gertrude and Alice looked around to see where they could best serve. "That's it!" Gertrude exclaimed one day while they were shopping, pointing to a sign on the side of a Ford car that said American Fund for French Wounded. "Why can't we help with that?"

Alice quickly contacted the headquarters for the organization and was told that they could distribute supplies, but first of all, they would need a car. Gertrude wrote to her relatives in America, and soon a cousin in New York raised enough money for a Ford car, which was shipped to them.

When they were notified that their car had arrived, Gertrude could hardly wait to pick it up. She was eager to try out her driving skills, which she had acquired only the year before. Alice, afraid that Gertrude overestimated her driving ability, went along with a great deal of trepidation.

On the way home in their new automobile it occurred to Gertrude that she knew how to go forward, but she hadn't the slightest notion how to reverse. "I must try to reverse," she told Alice.

"Oh no, Gertrude, wait until you're more experienced. I'm very happy that you can go forward."

But Gertrude had to try. She shifted gears, which sent the car hurtling backwards, to be sure, but only as far as some streetcar tracks, and there it stalled.

"Now look what you've done," Alice said crossly. "And a streetcar is coming!" Gertrude jumped from the car and cranked furiously. The streetcar slowed to a stop, and people got off and began giving advice.

"Another streetcar is coming!" Alice shrieked.

By this time Gertrude was also upset and anxious, but she continued to crank. The second streetcar stopped, and more people gathered around with advice. Still Gertrude cranked, but the car wouldn't start. Finally, red-faced and panting, Gertrude told the conductors, "There is only one thing to do—you must push the car off the track." A howl of approval went up from the crowd.

Gertrude settled herself in the driver's seat, and in no time their car was safely off the track. A large man threw off his coat and with two twists on the crank started the car. Gertrude tipped her hat and nodded her head to thank him, but under her breath, she said, "Why didn't he do that in the first place?"

"Providential!" Alice retorted. "You needed a lesson. I *told* you not to reverse until you had more experience."

When they reached home, Gertrude got out a bottle of wine and hit their new car over its shiny hood. "I hereby christen you 'Aunti' after my Aunt Pauline, who behaves admirably in emergencies and fairly well most other times, if properly flattered."

Gertrude and Alice went zealously about their volunteer work of distributing supplies to the French wounded, though in their military-style coats and helmet-shaped hats, they amused more people than they impressed. Alice was in charge of accounts. Gertrude drove Aunti and cheered discouraged and wounded soldiers with her infectious warmth.

Spending most of each day in a car was hard for Gertrude. It gave her little time for writing. Gradually, however, she grew accustomed to their mobile life, and she learned to be patient with the endless delays they encountered. One morning during an especially long wait, she picked up a pencil and wrote:

The Work

Not fierce and tender but sweet
This is our impression of the soldiers.

All too soon Alice was nudging her to start the car—to move along.

That afternoon they traveled through the valley of the Rhône. Gertrude ached to describe this landscape she loved so well. Every time they stopped to unload supplies,

Gertrude stayed in the car and wrote. Before nightfall she had completed a poem and a play. She sighed with relief. She could help with the war and write, too. Thank goodness!

For a time they were stationed at the Luxembourg Hotel in Nîmes. Here they met a young man, W. G. Rogers, who was with the ambulance unit from Amherst College. He had a ten-day leave and had come to Nîmes to get away from the war.

Gertrude liked him and behind his back affectionately referred to him as "Kiddie." She suggested to Alice that they invite him to ride along with them as they distributed supplies, thus giving him a vacation. Alice hesitated, for although she, too, liked Kiddie, she knew very well how much Gertrude longed to disrupt their schedule and go sightseeing herself. Finally Alice was persuaded. But on one condition: *She*, Alice, would extend the invitation. And would do so at once.

"Did he accept?" Gertrude asked eagerly when Alice returned.

"Yes, and furthermore he agreed to all the rules."

"*What* rules?"

"Rule number one:" Alice read from a small notebook, "Gertrude Stein must never be crowded because she needs to devote *all* her attention to driving. Rule number two: Gertrude Stein must never be kept waiting because this might delay our coming to a town before nightfall—Gertrude Stein does not drive well at night. Rule number three: This trip is being made for the American Fund for French Wounded, and we will not, *for any reason*, deviate from our schedule."

Umph, Gertrude thought to herself. She couldn't see how following such rules would appeal to a young man needing a vacation. In spite of them, she would make sure he had a good time!

As a matter of fact, all three had a fine time. They made side trips to every spot that hinted of interest, ate exceptionally well, and Gertrude conveniently misread road signs so she and Kiddie could see more of the countryside. All this, and still they delivered their supplies on time.

Even Alice grudgingly admitted they had successfully combined war work with pleasure. "But luck was with us," she quickly pointed out. "No credit is due Gertrude."

fifteen

"Make new friends—
create new interests."

The War is Over!

Suddenly everyone was kissing everyone else. Bells rang. Bartenders set out free kegs of beer. People danced in the streets. The cities of France were full of carnival gaiety.

But this was not true in the small villages. When the armistice was announced on November 11, 1918, Gertrude and Alice set out at once to spread the good news to the countryside. How wonderful, they thought, to tell a war-weary people of peace. Yet in village after village, they received the same unenthusiastic reception. The mayor greeted them, shook their hands rather sadly, and thanked them for coming. Gertrude and Alice were bewildered. Didn't these people want peace?

The answer came from a peasant whom they met walking along the road. "The armistice has been signed," Gertrude called to him as she slowed Aunti to a stop. At first the peasant's eyes lighted up and then they dimmed.

Slowly he shuffled over to the car and flashed a grin. "That's good," he said.

"That's good! Is that all you can say?"

"What else is there to say, Mademoiselle? The peace has come now, but it won't last—twenty years maybe, if we're lucky. We will scarcely have our fields cleared of war debris by that time."

"Why do you say that?" Gertrude demanded.

The old peasant smiled slyly. "I know it here," he said, pointing to his head.

"You know?"

"I know."

"And all the other villagers?"

"They all know, too."

"That old man really believes there will be another war," Alice said as they continued on their route.

Gertrude nodded. "I wish he hadn't sounded so convincing."

Soldiers began appearing on the road, never in groups, just single men with downcast eyes. Before long Gertrude could see the abandoned huts and trenches of the front lines. She stopped the car and looked around.

The sky was gray, the earth burned and desecrated. A few soldiers remained, sitting, staring into space or wandering aimlessly about. As Gertrude watched these forms, more specter than human, a deep sense of futility swept over her. Peace. She had yearned for it so long. But what difference did it make? The faces she saw here were not victorious or joyful, they were as tired as the landscape. Ideologies had not been decided on the battlefield. What was the fighting about then? She couldn't see an answer, all she could see was the result—wretched men, soulless, lost, dazed by their own folly.

Gertrude and Alice continued their volunteer work until May. Wearily they made their rounds, reminding each other that before long they could return home. Some days seemed too bleak to bear. When this happened, one of them would begin an encouraging tale starting with, "In May when we return to Paris . . ." They made all kinds of plans for their homecoming. Gertrude never tired of this, especially when Alice planned menus. She longed for the peace of their home and the smell of chicken being baked with butter and wine.

But their homecoming was better in story than in fact, for Paris was restless and so were the friends they had anticipated seeing. People flocked to 27 Rue de Fleurus, all of them trying to recapture the old life. To Gertrude they seemed foolish and shallow. Even Picasso irritated her, especially since he had begun using expressions from American Western movies. One night he called her "Pard," and she stalked out of the room. After that when Picasso tried to see her, she always said, "No, I am busy."

Over a year later Picasso came up to her at a party and said, "Oh let's forget it and be friends."

"No," she answered, "I cannot forget that easily."

But in two years she could forget, and they started being friends again.

During those two years, Gertrude struggled to regain her sense of identity. Before the war she had confidently believed that she was destined to become a part of history, an ideal she had held for as long as she could remember. Because of this belief, her behavior was sometimes more swashbuckling than her friends found reasonable. Gertrude thrived on their criticism. "Philistines," she was fond of saying, "do not understand genius. I am a genius, and I will act like one."

For years she had enjoyed always being onstage, always being the center of attention. She had written, managed, and for the most part, directed her own drama, cuing people around her to the proper response—until the war crashed in upon her. She bitterly resented its intrusion. Life could no longer be a series of theater acts played out on Saturday nights at the Stein salon, for the real drama that suddenly eclipsed all others—survival—left no room for capricious indulgences.

"After the war," she told herself firmly, "I will see again that I belong to history." But the war ended, and as she sat at her desk in the atelier trying to revive her old, full, unrestrained self-confidence, she had to admit that part of her self-styled magnificence had been no more than the loud buffoonery of youth. Such a conclusion left her bereft. She *needed* to believe in herself!

"Quit whimpering and face up to what's happening," Alice upbraided her when Gertrude talked about her problems. "Times have changed: Leo is no longer here; you refuse to see Picasso; Apollinaire is dead; you avoid Michael and Sarah. The old life is gone, Gertrude—forever! Admit it, but don't make it the end of your life. You're only forty-six years old. You still have the same intelligence and ambitions you had before the war. And your writing gives some hint of success. *Three Lives* has been published, *Tender Buttons*, too, and you must admit that Alfred Stieglitz's *Camera Work* was an appropriate place for the publication of the portraits you wrote about Picasso and Matisse. Make new friends—create new interests. If you can't do this now, you will never be great; you will only be a puppet manipulated by the adulation of other people."

Braced by the sharp truth of Alice's words, Gertrude

set out to develop new interests. Her first step was a fortunate one. She began making regular visits to a new lending library in the Rue de l'Odeon called Shakespeare & Co. Its proprietress, Sylvia Beach, catered to literary celebrities by displaying their pictures, and offered her patrons an excellent selection of reading material. Gertrude liked the shop so much that she became its first subscriber.

Shakespeare & Co. was such a success that it drew most of the literary and artistic people of Paris to it and became a place for people to be introduced and for names to be exchanged. One of those who came was Sherwood Anderson.

"He walked straight up to me and said, 'I wish to meet Gertrude Stein,' " Sylvia Beach told Gertrude.

"Then bring him to call. It will be amusing to talk to an American writer."

The next evening, Sherwood Anderson, his wife, and Sylvia Beach came to 27 Rue de Fleurus. As talk progressed, Anderson said, "You have been one of the principal influences of my life, Miss Stein."

"Of course!" Gertrude retorted brusquely. "Who else could have incited you to write such strong honest sentences."

When their guests left, Alice turned to Gertrude. "Sherwood Anderson will give you your confidence back. Make a friend of him."

"What do you mean?"

"You talk to him with authority, and he likes you for it. He's good for you." Unknown to Sherwood Anderson, he had passed the crucial test for anyone who wanted to entertain a lifelong friendship with Gertrude—Alice Toklas liked him.

As long as Sherwood Anderson remained in Paris,

Gertrude and Alice saw him often, and Gertrude's friendship with him deepened. When he returned to America, he promoted her work in every way he could. Critics who had previously laughed caustically over the "babbles of Steinese," now pulled in their horns and shuddered as Anderson's pen cut one after another of them down. He voiced his admiration for Gertrude in articles and speeches. In short, it seemed there was nothing he wouldn't do for her.

Gertrude, unaccustomed to such acclaim, could hardly believe her good fortune. She didn't know how to react. Demurely and out of character she wrote him coy notes telling him how much his approval of her writing meant. And he in turn wrote equally ridiculous replies. One of them began, "Gosh, I love you!"

As Alice predicted, Sherwood Anderson's overt admiration boosted Gertrude's morale immeasurably. Her self-confidence returned, as did her old sense of excitement and curiosity. Suddenly she wanted to be a part of the intellectual and artistic scene again, and she wanted to meet the people who were making it.

sixteen

"Go out and look at things, see them, hear them, feel them, then write about the real thing— don't write rumors."

"Where do I go to meet vigorous, creative people?" Gertrude asked Francis Picabia, a French painter, as they sat gossiping together one evening.

"They are all over Paris," Picabia said. "But why do you go to find them? Let them come to you. I will introduce you to a vigorous, creative person. He is a friend of mine, Tristan Tzara, leader of an artistic movement called Dadaism."

"Tristan Tzara? I've heard of him. Good. Bring him to the apartment."

The next afternoon Alice greeted Picabia and Tzara at the door. She ushered them into the atelier where Gertrude was waiting, seated them comfortably, and excused herself to get the tea tray. Gertrude and Picabia talked for a few minutes, then Gertrude looked sharply at Tzara. "Well," she blurted out, "you're certainly not what I expected. I see the gossipmongers are wrong again."

"I beg your pardon?" Tzara asked politely.

"I've been told that you're a maniac—that you intend to destroy the whole art world as a protest against the destruction of war. Is that correct?"

"Mademoiselle," Tzara said quietly, "I hated the war."

"Monsieur, I hated the war, too—lots of people hated the war. Do you think that gives you license to perpetuate its evil?"

"I would rather not talk about it," Tzara murmured.

"Not talk about it! What kind of leader are you that you don't want to talk about your movement? Do you know what I think? I think you are a good-natured young man imprisoned by your own words. Probably sometime you said, 'The world wants destruction? All right, let's show them what it is!' and someone heard you say that and went into the streets saying, 'Tristan Tzara says we should show the world what destruction is,' and suddenly you found yourself with a following."

Gertrude paused to give Tzara a chance to reply, but he only looked at the floor. Picabia twisted uncomfortably in his chair.

"I can forgive you for political naiveté," Gertrude continued, "but I can't forgive you for poking fun at poetry. I understand that Dadaist poetry is composed by throwing ideas into a hat and joining together whatever is drawn out . . ."

"Maybe I should go," Tzara said, getting up from his chair.

"You will *not* go!" Gertrude ordered. "If I am pricking your conscience, that's all to the good. Besides, we haven't had tea."

Obediently, Tzara sat down again.

Alice brought in the tea tray. She poured a cup for

Gertrude first and then one for each of their guests. As they drank their tea, Gertrude clarified her viewpoint. "You must understand, Tzara, I find you a very pleasant young man—it's your ideas I dislike."

"Don't worry about them," Tzara suddenly assured her. "Dadaism will soon be over."

Gertrude looked startled. "Do you think so?"

"Oh yes. We were very angry at first, but now we can be amused at ourselves." Tzara hesitated. "These things are difficult to explain. We are withdrawing quietly, Miss Stein, because some people don't like to see a movement ended by the protagonists being amused at themselves. They become angry and say, 'Just as I thought, cowards all of them!' "

"Why didn't you tell me this when you first arrived?" Gertrude demanded.

Tzara looked sheepish. "If you please, Mademoiselle, I was a little afraid of you. The tea has calmed me."

From that afternoon on, Gertrude held a fondness for Tzara. "He's kind of a crazy one," she would say affectionately. "He's really kind of a crazy one."

Gertrude felt maternal toward Tzara and smiled benevolently at his ways. But she was not tolerant toward anyone whose ego overshadowed her own. And neither was Alice.

Although they never discussed it, Alice adamantly kept Gertrude on a pedestal. She was ever vigilant for signs of a competitor, and when she spotted one, would quickly flay him away by whatever means best suited her purpose. Ezra Pound was one who felt the swiftness of her attack.

Gertrude and Alice met Ezra Pound at a party given by Grace Lounsbery. At first glance, his red beard, golden earring, and loud robust talk seemed to fill the room. Alice disliked him at once. "He laughs like a jackass and acts like one, too," she muttered to Gertrude. "Oh Lord, here he comes. No doubt he wants to meet you."

Gertrude watched him thrust his way through the crowd toward them. She, too, felt uneasy. He reminded her of Leo—the same nervous energy, the same belligerent self-confidence. Suddenly he was beside her, introducing himself, assuming that she wanted to meet him, telling her about his interest in Japanese prints, a passion Gertrude found especially irritating. She listened to his boastful flights with reserve. Pound didn't seem to notice. "Couldn't we go to 27 Rue de Fleurus?" he asked boldly. "I would like to see your paintings."

"All right," Gertrude agreed. "You get Miss Toklas' coat, and we will go."

Alice was furious. "I will serve him *nothing*," she said. "I think he is disgusting!"

Gertrude laughed, enjoying the drama that was unfolding.

Sitting in her chair by the iron stove in the atelier, Gertrude watched Ezra Pound as he went from one painting to another. He moved, she decided, like a tourist. Alice lurked in the corner, suspiciously watching everything he did.

"Well," Pound finally conceded. "You have some interesting pictures. Now let me tell you what they mean." Leaning up against a bookcase much as Leo would do, he launched into an explanation of each painting. So involved was he with his own words, he failed to notice that Gertrude was no longer humoring him, in fact she was angry. How dare he have the audacity to interpret art to *her*. She was the authority, not he!

"Mr. Pound," she interrupted him loudly, "you must go now. It is time Miss Toklas went to bed." Surprised at the intrusion into his discourse by such a mundane remark, Ezra Pound stared at Gertrude blankly. "Goodnight, Mr. Pound," she said firmly.

No sooner had the door closed than Alice pounced. "He thinks he can tell *you* something about art? He is a bigger fool than I thought. Why did you let him come in the first place? Anyone can see he has an inflated head with very little in it. And his manners are atrocious!"

Gertrude was strangely quiet. Then with a faint twinkle in her eye she said, "I let him come because he is a village explainer, fine if you are a village, but boring if you are not."

Alice looked at her quickly, her brown eyes snapping. "That's what you used to say about Leo."

"He reminded me of Leo."

"You mean," Alice said in astonishment, "you are feeling nostalgic about *Leo*?"

Gertrude got up abruptly. "Of course not!" she said.

A few days later, Ezra Pound came to the apartment again. During the afternoon he became so excited about making a point that he fell out of Gertrude's favorite armchair. The very idea that his awkwardness might have resulted in breaking a chair so annoyed Gertrude that after he left, she agreed with Alice—they would not let him come to 27 Rue de Fleurus again. She made her point clear when she met him walking in the Luxembourg Gardens one morning.

"I've been wanting to come see you," he said.

"No," Gertrude answered coldly, "I cannot see you because we are picking wildflowers, and Miss Toklas is suffering from an infected tooth." She hurried away before he could query further.

Some friends told her later that Pound was deeply hurt

because she didn't want to see him. Other friends said that he was saying, "Gertrude Stein? That old tub of guts! She's just a parasite sucking the glory out of other people's creative blood."

The same afternoon that Ezra Pound fell out of the armchair, he told Gertrude, "I know a fellow named T.S. Eliot. You should meet him. *There* is a poet." That was the first Gertrude had heard of T.S. Eliot, but soon everyone she met was saying the same thing. Before long Lady Rothermere, who was working with T.S. Eliot on *The Criterion,* the literary review magazine that he edited, sent a special invitation for Gertrude and Alice to meet him at her house.

Gertrude was dubious about going. She questioned the discernment of others, especially in matters of whom she should or should not meet. But finally, because of Alice's urging, she decided they could spare the time. No sooner had Alice started making a new evening dress to wear to the event, however, than Lady Rothermere and T.S. Eliot appeared at the door. "Put your needle away," Gertrude whispered to Alice. "We don't have to go now."

The discussion between Gertrude and T.S. Eliot began at once. They talked about split infinitives. "On whose authority do you use them?" he asked.

"Well, Henry James for one," Gertrude replied evenly.

T.S. Eliot didn't say anything for a minute, then he quickly turned his attention to *The Criterion.* He said he would print something of Gertrude's, but he wanted something new and fresh, her very latest thing. "I will send you my very latest thing," she promised.

After T.S. Eliot and Lady Rothermere left, Gertrude wrote a portrait of T.S. Eliot and entitled it *The Fifteenth of November* because that was the date. This would certainly be her most current work. She sent it immediately.

That night, as she sat at her desk, she thought about her afternoon with Eliot. Some people called him "the major." The description was apt, for he did look very British and very severe, even though he came from St. Louis, Missouri. But a major would look more youthful. She thought Eliot carried an aura of age about him. He seemed an old soul, fated to murmur oracles of uncertain doom till the end of his days.

Soon after T.S. Eliot's call, Gertrude and Alice left Paris to spend the winter in Saint Rémy, a spot they had grown to love during the war. Gertrude had seen enough avant-garde people for a while. She longed for the peace of country living. In the quiet valley of the Rhône, she could talk with simple peasant people who took their wisdom or lack of it with great good humor.

As Gertrude walked on dusty country roads and absorbed the uncomplicated landscapes all around her, a stillness replaced the last vestiges of melancholy she had felt as an aftermath of war. She began to meditate for long periods of time on grammar and poetical forms. As a result, she wrote essays on paragraphs, sentences, grammar, and vocabulary. In one essay called *An Elucidation,* she articulated her own problems in writing and told how she solved them.

When Alice read *An Elucidation,* she said, "You should be a teacher."

"Yes, I've been thinking the same thing. Maybe, if I find a bright student, I will be."

The first person to greet them on their return to Paris was a shy, tall, and exceedingly handsome young man with a letter of introduction from Sherwood Anderson. The young man's name was Ernest Hemingway.

Gertrude invited him in. He wanted to talk about writing, and with intensely interested eyes he watched Gertrude as she spoke. Finally he, too, began to talk, and Gertrude learned that he was twenty-three, a Paris correspondent for a Canadian newspaper, and a man with a burning desire to be a writer. His wife, Hadley, wanted Gertrude and Alice to have dinner with them the following week.

"Yes," Gertrude said, "we will come."

"Why must we have dinner with them?" Alice asked after Hemingway left. "He doesn't seem any different from countless other young men who have come to see you."

"But he is different. He can listen—really *listen.* He will make a good student."

They went. After dinner Hemingway got out his manuscripts to show Gertrude. She thought the poems quite good, the short stories acceptable, but she didn't think the novel good at all. "Too much description," she said, "and it's all bad. Good description doesn't herald itself, it weaves a background. Start all over again and this time, *concentrate.* Go out and look at things, see them, hear them, feel them, then write about the real thing—don't write rumors."

After that, Gertrude always seemed to find time for Hemingway. They took long walks together, discussing the practical side of Hemingway's life. How was he to write and be a correspondent, too? "You cannot," Gertrude advised. "You cannot dissipate the passion you need for creative work. Save your money for a year and then decide that you will only write creatively."

Yes, Hemingway agreed, that's what he would do.

Then one day Hemingway appeared at 27 Rue de Fleurus so discouraged and downcast that Gertrude could hardly get him to talk. Finally he told her that his wife was pregnant. He would have to give up his dreams of being a writer and be a father instead.

"Hemingway," Gertrude said, "what if all the men in the world gave up their dreams because an unexpected child came along? There would be precious few dreams left! You can still save your money—if you have enough courage, you can still be a writer."

Fired by Gertrude's straight talk, Hemingway left Paris for almost a year and saved his money. When he came back, Gertrude saw that he had begun to imitate her way of using words to circle back upon themselves so the reader might feel a depth of emotion. His stories began to sell.

Hemingway tried to repay Gertrude for her advice and encouragement in many ways, but the way she appreciated most was his encouraging Ford Maddox Ford to print *The Making of Americans* serially in *The Transatlantic Review*, a magazine published in Paris. When Ford agreed, Gertrude said, "Hemingway, no matter how many feuds we may have in the future, I will always have a soft spot in my heart for you because of this favor."

Gertrude learned later that Hemingway liked to repeat this story and that he usually added a line of his own: "Some people are right only half of the time, but Gertrude, she is right all of the time."

seventeen

"Criticism is easier to live with than praise."

Having found the bright student she sought in Hemingway and having coached him to success, Gertrude now directed her energy toward promoting the publication of her own works. She especially wanted *The Making of Americans* published in book form. When she learned that Robert McAlmon, the young director of the Contact Press, was in Paris, she instructed Alice to send him an invitation for tea. If anyone would publish *The Making of Americans*, she felt it would be he.

McAlmon graciously accepted the invitation. As he and Gertrude sipped tea, they first talked about biographies and the novels of Trollope. Then Gertrude astutely turned to discussing her unpublished manuscripts. "When *The Making of Americans* is published," she said, "I think it would be more marketable if it were brought out in six volumes over a period of two years, don't you?" She handed him the manuscript that was lying on the table in front of them.

"No," McAlmon answered, quickly skimming through the pages. "Since it has no apparent divisions, it should be published in one volume."

"If it were printed in one volume, would it find a market?"

"Yes."

"And you think it would be worth taking a chance on?"

"Yes."

"Good! When shall I send it to you?" McAlmon looked startled. "My friends will buy fifty advance copies," Gertrude said, as if everything were settled. McAlmon carefully put the manuscript back on the table. But before he left that afternoon, Gertrude had exacted a promise from him to publish *The Making of Americans.*

"He's really going to publish it!" Gertrude gloated.

"Don't set your hopes too high," Alice admonished. "Robert McAlmon may renege at the last minute—after all, you tricked him."

But Robert McAlmon had given his word, and before long the Contact Press sent the exciting news that the manuscript was being set in type. Soon after, the first sheets of proof arrived. Gertrude could hardly wait to start correcting them. Then she saw the staggering number of mistakes on every page. "How can there be so many?" she groaned.

The French printer, Maurice Darantière, was evidently totally bewildered by Gertrude's repetitious sentences and lack of punctuation. In setting the type the printer had repeated when he shouldn't and didn't when he should. Sometimes he had deleted whole sentences. After the first week, Alice, who had volunteered to help correct proof, claimed her mind was boggled.

"Could you go on with it if we worked at Saint-Rémy?" Gertrude asked.

"I could try."

With Gertrude urging speed at every step, Alice quickly packed their things. They drove to the valley of the Rhone and registered at the Pernollet Hotel. There they began work in earnest.

Each morning they emerged from the hotel with streamers of proof, camp chairs, and an abundant lunch of at least one chicken, a variety of cheeses, fruit, and wine. Although Gertrude was always in a hurry to start correcting, she took time to find just the right spot for working. "An environment that establishes a good frame of mind is the most important fact of the day," she liked to inform Alice, who sometimes showed signs of impatience.

Gertrude's favorite working places were sun-exposed areas by a stream where they could watch the sheep wind their way up the mountainside. The combination of sun, stream, mountain, and grazing sheep soothed her. She didn't mind checking each page over four times, for she had little sense of hours passing when she was at peace.

They were making good headway when Alice's glasses broke. She tried to work without them, but finally had to admit that her eyes had completely given out. Gertrude struggled on alone. She might have become discouraged had she not been absorbed in rereading the manuscript, something she hadn't done for almost twenty years.

The beginning she thought especially good. It related a tale about a young man who dragged his father through an orchard. "Stop!" the father cried when they passed a certain tree. "I didn't drag my father beyond this point."

The story made her think of Leo and his persistent struggle to be freed from the past. Would he ever succeed? She doubted it.

Hearsay informed her that Leo was living in Florence, and like a cat fascinated by its tail, was ever-circling, in pursuit of the answers to self-analysis. How dull he would be, obsessed with his own ailments, always eating nuts, forever being an authority. She was surprised he had any friends at all. But apparently he had maintained some contacts. And he had a wife! After more than thirteen years of courtship, he had finally married Nina Auzias. Gertrude winced. What a terrible husband he would make.

Although friends gossiped about Leo frequently, Gertrude had seen him only once since he left 27 Rue de Fleurus. One day shortly after they returned to Paris from their war efforts, she and Alice were driving in traffic so snarled that it came to a halt. While waiting for it to move again, Gertrude glanced at the man in the car next to her. At the same time he looked at her. Gertrude nodded her head in brief greeting and then stared directly ahead.

"To whom did you bow?" Alice asked afterwards.

"Leo Stein," Gertrude answered shortly.

By the fall of 1925 Gertrude and Alice were ready to return to Paris. The proofs were almost finished, and Gertrude had started writing *A Novel* and a short piece called *Natural Phenomena*. The summer had been profitable.

Among young writers, the word had spread that Gertrude Stein could work a kind of magic. Hadn't she done so for Ernest Hemingway? Scores of hopeful young men greeted her arrival in Paris. Each of them wanted an audience. Would she read a poem, a play, a novel? Would she give advice? Would she work her magic, whatever it was, so they could be lucky, like Hemingway?

Obligingly, Gertrude sat in the atelier and, with a sandal dangling from the toe of her woolen sock, held court. She listened intently to all who came. To young men who had talent, she gave criticism and thoughtful advice. To young men who had no talent, she gave nothing; they were not encouraged to return.

A mid-winter visit from Edith Sitwell interrupted Gertrude's season of holding court. A year before, Miss Sitwell had reviewed *Geography and Plays*, a book Gertrude had published with The Four Seas Company in Boston in 1922. In the review Miss Sitwell had said that the book was full of silliness. But some time later in an issue of the London *Vogue*, she had retracted her previous opinion, after having spent almost a year reading little else. "*Geography and Plays*," she wrote, "is a very important and beautiful book." When Gertrude read this, she and Edith became fast friends.

"You should lecture, Gertrude," Edith suggested when she came to call. "It would increase your reading audience. The Literary Society at Cambridge would be a good place to start."

Gertrude laughed at the idea. "I'm a writer, not a speaker," she replied.

Not long after that, an official-looking letter arrived. Alice quickly perused its contents and cried out, "Gertrude! The Literary Society at Cambridge wants you to speak to them."

"Speak to them?" Gertrude repeated, her face suddenly pale. "When?"

"The letter says you can choose the date, but they would prefer it to be sometime this spring."

Gertrude slumped deep into her chair.

"Imagine," Alice chattered gaily, "you're to speak at an

erudite gathering in England! It *will* be nice to be back in English society."

"Alice," Gertrude interrupted weakly, "we can't go."

"What?"

"We *can't* go," Gertrude said louder, shifting about in her chair. Alice stared at her blankly. "I can't work in England," Gertrude said flatly. "So going is out of the question. Send a reply at once saying it is impossible."

"But you won't have to work. We can go and come back immediately. You've delayed work much longer than that other times." Alice looked at Gertrude sternly. "That is *not* the real reason. What is it—why won't you go to England?"

Gertrude lowered her eyes under Alice's probing gaze. Then looking up at her, childlike and very frightened, she whispered, "Oh Alice, I couldn't speak in front of all those people. I would be scared to death."

Alice knelt down beside her. "But Gertrude," she pleaded, "couldn't you adjust to the idea? It's such a wonderful opportunity."

Gertrude shook her head. "I would like to, but, well . . . I just couldn't!"

Frustrated and bewildered by the fear that was keeping Gertrude from enjoying the fame she so desperately wanted, Alice nevertheless sent a reply to Cambridge saying that Miss Stein thanked them for their invitation, but found it impossible to accept.

For several days Gertrude was inconsolable about the Cambridge invitation. Then a letter came from Edith Sitwell:

> The Cambridge Literary Society writes to me saying you have refused to accept their invita-

> tion. They are devastated, as is the Society of Oxford, who was only waiting for your affirmative reply to Cambridge to send their own. My dear Gertrude, your refusal is out of the question. You simply *must* change your mind.

Under this kind of positive urging, Gertrude relented. "I guess Edith Sitwell is right," she sighed. "All right, we will go."

Alice was overjoyed. But Gertrude was more depressed about accepting than about not accepting. "I thought I had become quite courageous during the war," she told Alice. "And when the war was over, I thought I needn't be frightened again. But now I see that peace holds much greater terrors than war. Besides, what am I to speak on? I can't think of a thing."

The day for their departure drew near. Still Gertrude could think of nothing to lecture about. One cold dreary afternoon she took her Ford car to a shop to have it repaired. As was her habit, she sat in the garage and watched while the mechanics worked. Suddenly she felt an urge to write. Taking out pen and paper, she began the lecture she had waited so long to formulate:

> There is singularly nothing that makes a difference a difference in beginning and in the middle and in ending except that each generation has something different at which they are all looking.

Four hours passed before she looked up. The car was long finished and she was chilled to the bone, but her lecture was completed. At the top of the first page she wrote

Composition as Explanation. Stuffing the lecture into her pocket, she hurried home.

Now that Gertrude had something to say, the problem of how to say it arose. When friends learned of her dilemma, they all had advice to offer. Some said she must talk slowly and never look down; others said she must talk quickly and never look up. As usual, Alice's practical advice was best. "Be natural," she said. "Your warm voice will attract the audience, and your uncommon good sense will hold them. It will not matter whether you look up or down, whether you read slowly or quickly."

When Gertrude and Alice arrived in England, Gertrude's stage fright had grown to such proportions that she could hardly eat. The afternoon of the lecture she was so frightened she was ill. Edith Sitwell's brother, Osbert, comforted her by telling of his own fear of audiences. They passed the afternoon by humorously suggesting different ways they could overcome stage fright.

All too soon, however, it was time for the lecture. Gertrude donned a blue robe given to her by the wife of Jo Davidson, the well-known sculptor. "Alice," Gertrude said, "I am going to do this thing. If I don't, it will be because my heart fails me in front of all those people. That being the case, carry me off and read the lecture—it's a damn good one!"

Resolutely poised, she marched onstage accompanied by Alice, who looked like a "gypsy acolyte," as one of the Oxford students later described her. In a clear steady voice Gertrude began *Composition as Explanation.* When she finished, murmurs of approval flowed up from the crowd.

The discussion period that followed lasted for over an hour. "Why do you think you are doing the right thing to write the way you do?" someone asked her.

"It is not a question of what I think or of what anyone else thinks," she replied. "I have been going my own way for twenty years and now you want to hear me lecture. Your conclusion is all that matters to you and mine to me."

Two young men, who had apparently come with the intention of heckling, popped up in different parts of the auditorium. "You say that everything is the same and everything is different. How can that be?" they asked at the same time.

"Why," Gertrude purred congenially, "just look at you two dear boys. You jump up together, that is the same thing; and surely you admit that the two of you are always different."

From Cambridge, Gertrude and Alice went to Oxford. This time Gertrude looked forward to the lecture. Ascending the stage with confidence, she charmed the audience at once. The discussion period was even more vigorous than at Cambridge. Radiant and very pleased, Gertrude answered the questions directed to her with wisdom and good humor.

"How do you feel?" Alice whispered as they walked off the stage.

"Like a prima donna," Gertrude answered, "but a very tired one."

The Sitwells wanted them to stay in England. "No," said Gertrude, "we must return to Paris tomorrow."

"But," Edith objected, "you have lived with criticism for many years. Now you should enjoy the praise due you."

"Criticism is easier to live with than praise," Gertrude replied. "No real artist needs criticism. If he needs criticism, then he is no artist. And since he doesn't *need* it, he doesn't have to assimilate it into his life. However, real artists *need* praise. And since they need it, they have to assimilate it into their lives, which takes time and can be exhausting if there is too much of it."

eighteen

"We only make a change when we know that it will become regular."

Gertrude was fifty-two, and her future had never looked brighter. The prestige she had earned lecturing in England had spread to France. People who hadn't taken her seriously now viewed her writing in a new light. Everywhere she went, she was greeted with congratulations and requests for copies of *Composition as Explanation.* The lecture was being published in England by Virginia and Leonard Woolf's Hogarth Press and in America by *The Dial*, a magazine devoted to the encouragement of avant-garde authors. Marianne Moore was its editor.

Spurred on by the warm praise that surrounded her, Gertrude felt more compelled than ever to write. But she needed a new inspiration. In the past, cubism had stimulated both her mind and her will. Now, although cubism was still developing through the work of such painters as Juan Gris and Francis Picabia, the excitement of its creation was past—she needed a new vision.

She found what she was searching for at the Galerie Druet where a group of painters known as the neo-romantics were exhibiting. These artists, among them Pavel Tchelitchew and Eugene Berman, were reacting against the abstraction and harsh lines of cubism by painting recognizable forms in pastel colors. Gertrude looked and looked at these paintings and then began a novel which she called *Lucy Church Amiably*. Feeling lyrical, she wrote a key sentence in order to establish a rhythm for the work: "Select your song she said and it was done and then she said and it was done with a nod and then she bent her head in the direction of the falling water. Amiably."

All through the winter of 1926 and into the spring of 1927, Gertrude wrote under the influence of the neo-romantics. As she worked, she felt as if she were surrounded by a penumbra of warmth and good luck. Nothing marred her feeling of extraordinary happiness until one day in early May a note came carrying the news that Juan Gris had died.

Gertrude read the message through twice to make certain she was not mistaken. Then she pulled the curtains at 27 Rue de Fleurus and went into mourning. For days she sat alone with her thoughts and grieved. She couldn't forget how Juan Gris had lived in poverty through the war years, beset by discouragement and ill-health. But he had courage—always Juan Gris had courage!

In the dim light she looked around the atelier at the familiar paintings that had meant so much to her for so long. Among them were two she had purchased within the last three years from Juan Gris, *The Green Cloth* and *Dish of Pears*. What drew her to his work? she wondered. Why did she feel such an intimacy with him and also with his paintings? A kind of mystical quality, she decided. A kind of mystical quality coupled with his intellectual approach and warmth of expression.

Picasso came to sit with her and was sad, too, thinking if he shared her grief it would help. But he only irritated her. "You have no right to mourn Juan Gris' death," Gertrude said angrily. "You did not know his meaning."

"I *did* know his meaning—you know very well I did. But you, Gertrude, why is your grief so great? You have scarcely noticed him for years."

"You do not know what I have done or not done, Pablo. I helped support him through the war and kept up with his work. He needed to work alone and I respected that, but I loved him. You know nothing about it, Pablo, *nothing*. Near the end of his life he had perfection; he joined beauty and perfection and from this he created something that was measurable, yes, definitely measurable. No, you do not know, Pablo, you do not know!" Picasso went away shaking his head sadly, but Gertrude was too grief-stricken to care.

The next day Alice pulled the curtains back. "You are doing the memory of Juan Gris a great disservice by mourning so long, Gertrude. Besides I'm not going to live in darkness any longer. The dead are dead, but life must go on. A change is what you need. We've talked for several months of having electric lights installed in the atelier. Let's do it now."

Half-heartedly, Gertrude agreed. But when the lights were installed and she saw how well the paintings looked when they were clearly illuminated, her mild interest changed to enthusiasm. Friends began dropping in to see the renovation at 27 Rue de Fleurus. "How wonderful!" Mildred Aldrich exclaimed when she saw the lights. "But tell me, Gertrude, why did it take you so long to put them in?"

"Because," Gertrude replied, "when you are way ahead with your head, you are naturally old-fashioned and regular with your daily life. I am way ahead with my head so we are very old-fashioned and regular with our daily life. Lights became necessary because we needed a change. But now that the change is made, the lights will become regular. We only make a change when we know that about it, that it will become regular."

The previous year, right after Gertrude and Alice returned from England, they had looked for a country home in the valley of the Rhône, but had found nothing. Now, with another summer upon them, Gertrude was eager to look again. One day driving through Belignin, Gertrude suddenly stopped the car. "There!" she pointed excitedly. "There is our house." Alice peered through the hazy sunlight. On a hillside among trees and garden plots stood a country home that looked as if it were indeed the house of their dreams.

"It's beautiful!" Alice cried. "But it looks occupied."

Gertrude quickly shifted gears. "No matter. We will drive into town and ask who owns it."

A kindly farmer was agent for the house. "It's rented now," he told them, "by an army officer."

"How long will he stay?" Alice inquired.

"I have no way of knowing, Mademoiselle."

"He won't stay long," Gertrude said confidently. "And when he moves from the house, we want it."

"Have you looked at it?"

"Yes, from across the valley. You will notify us when the army man is gone?"

"*Oui,* Mademoiselle." The farmer took off his hat and scratched his head. "I will notify you, but how do you know you want the house if you haven't seen it closer than from across the valley?"

"I know—here!" Gertrude replied, buoyantly pointing to her head.

Driving back to Paris, Gertrude was elated over their find. Suddenly she ran her hand through her hair. "Alice," she said, "when we arrive home, I want you to cut my hair."

The Duchesse de Clermont-Tonnerre, whom Gertrude greatly admired as a person and as an author, had recently cut her hair and had been urging Gertrude to do the same. "As soon as I summon enough courage," Gertrude had told her. Today she had enough courage!

Early the next morning, Alice began cutting. She cut all day long. By evening there was nothing left but a little cap on the top. As Alice cut, Gertrude held her glasses at a distance and experimented with reading a book one word at a time. Finally Alice put the shears down. "Sherwood Anderson is coming to call this evening, remember? We just have time to change our clothes."

When Anderson rang the bell, Alice was dressed and had already prepared some refreshments. Gertrude was still in the bedroom. "Please sit down," Alice said. "Gertrude will be here soon."

But "soon" turned into fifteen minutes, and still Gertrude did not appear. Alice stepped to the bottom of the stairs. "Gertrude, please hurry," she called. "Sherwood is waiting for you."

"I can't come down," Gertrude called from the bedroom.

"Why can't you?"

"I haven't anything to wear."

"Of course you have something to wear," Alice said impatiently. "Your wardrobe is full of clothes."

"I mean on my head," Gertrude said weakly.

"Gertrude come down!" Alice ordered. "You are going to have to face the world sometime with your new haircut, and Sherwood is a good one to start with."

Timorously, Gertrude started down the stairs. When Sherwood saw her, he gasped, "Why, Gertrude, it's wonderful! You look like a monk."

Gertrude looked at him sharply. "If you are blaspheming the Church, Sherwood, you deserve to roast in hell."

Sherwood held out his hand. "Gertrude, if the Church were half as beautiful as you, the good Lord could take a vacation. You've never looked better. I mean it . . . you've never looked better."

Gertrude beamed happily and threw herself into the evening's talk. Sherwood Anderson's spontaneous approval of her haircut set her at ease. Now she could be confident about appearing in society, for if Sherwood thought she looked good, then of course she did!

By the summer of 1928 the army officer who lived in the house they liked in Belignin was transferred to Morocco. When Gertrude was notified of this, she was so happy that she went out and bought a new car, which they left unnamed, and a new poodle, which they named Basket. They left for Belignin as soon as Alice could pack.

Their new house was indeed all they had dreamed of and more. "It is the greenest of our valleys by good angels tenanted," Gertrude wrote to a friend. Though close to the village, it was unusually private because of the fence in front and the hills behind. Poplars and acacias accented the deep-roofed, gray stone house. Vegetable gardens lay between the house and the hills. Such a wonderful house demanded at least half of their attention, Gertrude decided. They would spend the spring and summer in Belignin and the fall and winter in Paris.

During their first summer in Belignin, Alice became an expert farmer, gardener, and veterinarian. Gertrude became expert in doing nothing—or at least it appeared that she was doing nothing. She loved the formal flower garden behind the house, where she could sit in the hot sun and listen to the sounds around her. She meditated for days on what a victory it was for a person of her temperament to be able to do nothing.

Basket the poodle joined her in the garden, noisily lapping milk from a bowl that sat beside her chair. Gertrude listened. Why did he start and end when he did and then pause and start again? For that matter, why did people start sentences when they did, then pause and start again? The rhythm of a dog lapping milk and a person making sentences were similar. Yes, definitely similar.

When Gertrude wasn't resting in the sun, she took walks in the countryside and talked with the farmers and their wives. She loved these people and their good-natured ways. The men discussed crops with her, and the women asked her advice about child-rearing. On both subjects Gertrude gave sober counsel.

As long as she and Alice stayed in Belignin, Gertrude was happy and relaxed. But each year when they returned to Paris, she became more obsessed with the pile of manuscripts that stood on the table in the atelier. Although she had published *Three Lives*, *The Making of Americans*, and several smaller works, most of her writing hadn't interested publishers. Even those who sympathized with her innovative style thought she was a poor business risk. By the winter of 1930, Gertrude was so discouraged that she took to her bed.

Alice tried to console her, but Gertrude only moaned and turned her face to the wall. Day after day Gertrude's condition was no better; in fact her depression grew steadily worse. Alice decided that something had to be done. One morning she left the apartment and was gone all day. When she returned in the evening, she was flushed with excitement. "Get out of bed, Gertrude," she called from the door, "your manuscripts are going to be published."

In a short time Gertrude appeared at the top of the stairs. "Alice, be serious!"

"I am serious. I've spent the whole day at the Maurice Darantière Press learning how to organize a publishing company so we can publish your books. All we need now is money."

For once Gertrude was speechless. Also she was deeply touched. Alice was by nature shy. She hated to be in the limelight. For her to spend a whole day discussing such a venture had taken great courage. Gertrude came downstairs and sat in her favorite chair. She didn't speak for a while. Then she said, "This is a wonderful thing you have done. Thank you very much. I will get the money for you."

The next week Gertrude sold Picasso's *Girl with a Fan.* With these funds at her disposal, Alice began to follow step by step the plan suggested to her. Before long she had established a publishing house in every detail except a name.

Up to this time Gertrude had stayed discreetly out of Alice's way, but now she came to the fore. "We will call the publishing house Plain Edition," she said. "And the books will be wrapped in plain blue paper. That way they will be inexpensive and everyone who wants to can buy one."

Lucy Church Amiably was published first, and although Alice had some problems with distribution, by clever maneuvering, she managed to put it in most of the important bookstores in Paris. For days Gertrude walked about the streets taking a naïve delight in seeing her books in the shop windows. There they were, her books, her name, her ideas. Now, with Alice publishing her manuscripts, she need never worry about publication again.

When Gertrude and Alice left for Belignin in 1932, they were unusually tired. Publishing was an exhausting business even though sales were not discouraging. They looked forward to the peace of their country home. The first evening after they arrived, Gertrude wrote on a scrap of paper: "A home is a home is a sanctuary is a relief yes a relief from too much and tiredness."

Summer brought days of hot sun for Gertrude and a plethora of vegetables and fruits for Alice. The tiredness began to go, but not enough to lure Gertrude away from the country. She decided she was still too tired to return to Paris in the fall. After all, why should they go? Gertrude reasoned with herself. Plain Edition was the only business they had to tend to, and its direction was well set.

Since the publication of *Lucy Church Amiably*, Gertrude and Alice had brought out three other works under the Plain Edition imprint: *Before The Flowers of Friendship Faded, Friendship Faded; How To Write; Operas and Plays;* and they had plans to do a fourth: *Matisse, Picasso and Gertrude Stein With Two Shorter Stories.* The two women had agreed that when these five pieces were distributed, they would stop. And they would start up again only if necessary.

A long lazy autumn set in. Warmly contented, Gertrude became whimsical, almost playful. "Why don't you write your autobiography?" she teased Alice.

"Because," said Alice, elbow deep in harvesting the abundant food crop the land had produced, "I have neither the time nor the inclination."

"Then I will have to do it for you," Gertrude said.

One night soon afterward, she went to her desk and began *The Autobiography of Alice B. Toklas:*

> I was born in San Francisco, California. I have in consequence always preferred living in a temperate climate but it is difficult, on the continent of Europe or even America, to find a temperate climate and live in it.

For six weeks Gertrude worked, then she sent the finished manuscript to W.A. Bradley, an agent in Paris. His reply came by return mail:

> I have forwarded your manuscript to Harcourt Brace. Congratulations—it's a sure hit!

Now things happened so fast that Gertrude could hardly believe all that was being said and done. Harcourt Brace accepted the manuscript enthusiastically and, as W.A. Bradley had predicted, *The Autobiography of Alice B. Toklas* was an immediate success. Almost overnight, Gertrude exploded into fame.

Her lifetime ambition of being famous had become a reality, writ larger than even she had ever anticipated. Reviews poured in saying how relieved the critics were to discover that she was sane after all and that she *could* write. "Come to America!" friends and lecture agencies alike urged her. "Come to America and gather in your laurels."

"No, I will not go to America," Gertrude said. "Lecture to all those people? I should say not!" But as more and more friends wrote and the idea penetrated deeper into Gertrude's mind, she began to think it might be rather nice to see America again. Alice thought so, too.

Gradually they began making plans, pretending they *might* go to America, until one day they were both startled to discover that they had made so many plans there was nothing to do but say they *were* going. "We have finally said 'yes, we are going to America,'" Gertrude wrote at her desk that night. "I am a little frightened and so is Alice, but we *are* going. And while we are there we will see and and we will hear and we will be very very famous."

nineteen

"After all, I haven't changed.
I am still me."

Before going to America, Gertrude anticipated a period of quiet in which she could organize her thoughts and prepare lectures. But a quiet life became impossible. Fame suddenly embraced her so tenaciously that she feared it would dissipate all her energies. "I don't like it!" she complained to Alice. "I don't like so many people coming and calling and writing, as if I were a new discovery. After all, I haven't changed. I am still me."

"Enjoy it, Gertrude," Alice replied. "This is what you have sought after all your life."

Had she? Gertrude wondered. No, she didn't think so. She had wanted to be historical, it was true, and to this end she had struggled, but all the time she had insisted on a "daily island" life where she could work and be quiet. Now her peaceful core was shattered with so much talk and flattery that she hadn't time for either working or thinking. Instead of writing at night, she wandered through the house like a shade in search of her old ambitious self. When she tried to put words down on paper, nothing came.

She was troubled, too, by the money she was receiving from America, more than she had ever hoped to earn. She liked money and she liked the idea of being rich, but why did people pay so much for *The Autobiography of Alice B. Toklas*, something she had intended as a joke. She was perplexed by the values this revealed, and she couldn't identify with them. In fact, she couldn't identify with any of what was happening, and she was afraid that success might change her basic nature.

Most of all she feared that in the midst of such immense recognition she would lose herself—if she hadn't already. "Who am I?" she asked herself repeatedly. "Who is Gertrude Stein?" No matter how she approached this problem, an answer would not come. She brooded until one morning Alice reminded her that the day for their departure to America was close at hand. The search for identity would have to wait.

From aboard the *S.S. Champlain* on October 24, 1934, Gertrude saw Staten Island for the first time in twenty-five years. It was impressive and fresh-looking, so white and green, but the silhouette of New York City was disappointing. How small it looked! Leaning against the ship's railing, Gertrude watched New York Harbor silently glide toward her in the morning mist.

Suddenly she heard a commotion below her and saw a boatload of newspapermen pull up beside the ship. When they spotted Gertrude, they shouted and threw their hats into the air. At first she couldn't believe they were waving at her. Alice nudged her. "Smile back, Gertrude, the American press has arrived."

"To interview me!" Gertrude exclaimed.

"Of course. Wave to them!"

Utterly astonished, Gertrude watched the reporters scramble up the rope ladders that had been lowered for them and push their way toward her. Then she started chuckling. In France she had spent agonizing hours consumed with worry about her identity. Apparently she would have no such problem to wrestle with in America. At least the press seemed to know well enough who she was.

Gertrude met the reporters with confidence. Those who came to ridicule were easily won over by her good humor and wise answers. Those who were already in sympathy with her personality and writing were more captivated than ever. As a result, most New York City newspapers ran front page stories with blazing headlines, "Gertrude Stein Comes to Town." Times Square heralded her with a message in blinking lights: "Gertrude Stein Is Here."

Lectures were to begin at once, the first one sponsored by the Museum of Modern Art, where she was to speak about "Pictures." Preparations had been meticulously made and everything was ready—except Gertrude, who had again come down with a bad case of stage fright. "I can't do it, Alice," she whispered. "It is impossible! Listen . . . I have no voice. I cannot speak." Alice wasted no time in calling a doctor.

When the doctor arrived he looked into Gertrude's throat. "What do you see?" Gertrude asked after he removed the tongue depressor.

"Nothing."

"Nothing?"

"No infection. Your throat is constricted, however, as if from fright."

"Well I'm not surprised!" Gertrude exploded, suddenly able to talk. "I'm scheduled to do a public lecture in a short time, and I'm scared to death."

The doctor peered at Gertrude over his glasses. "Aren't you Gertrude Stein?"

"Yes."

The doctor was silent as he snapped his bag closed, then he said, "I have long admired your courage, Miss Stein. For that reason I am going to your lecture tonight. My son is coming with me. He, too, admires your courage." Tipping his hat, the doctor quickly left.

Gertrude stared at the closed door. "Oh damn, damn, damn!" she finally muttered. "Get my dress ready, Alice. It's just as it was in England. I *have* to perform."

Once onstage, Gertrude quickly established rapport with the audience. Feeling their good will and confidence, she gave herself to them heart and soul. The soothing depth of her voice and the rhythm of her words seemed to gather the crowd into one mind, and she guided them smoothly through the intricacies of her thinking.

When she stopped speaking, there was silence for a moment, then thunderous, explosive applause. "Identity?" Gertrude mused, glowing from the ovation. She wouldn't give it another thought. Why should she? America loved her, and she loved America. That was enough for the time being.

For the next six months, Gertrude lived in the certain knowledge that wherever she went she was a celebrity. Her popularity penetrated every social level. When she appeared for lectures, police had to hold back crowds so often that it was finally decided that no more than five hundred tickets could be sold.

Every minute was full for her and Alice. When Gertrude wasn't lecturing, other exciting events filled their time. Eleanor Roosevelt gave a tea for them at the White House. George Gershwin entertained them by running through the score of his new musical, *Porgy and Bess*. In Chicago they went to see Gertrude's opera, *Four Saints in Three Acts*, which she had written in 1927 and Virgil Thomson had set to music. Gertrude was pleased. The all-Negro cast was effective and the settings and costumes by Florine Stettheimer were stunning, but the libretto didn't seem to be her own. Had she really written it, and if so when? It was hard to remember. But yes, it was quite nice.

There was so much to see and do that friends persuaded Gertrude and Alice to travel by plane. At first Gertrude was apprehensive about flying, but once in the air she was delighted, especially since she could see for the first time what the cubists were trying to do. "In their painting they are creating the cubes and planes of the earth as seen from the air," she said. "But most of them have never traveled in a plane. They saw the vision in their minds—this is a great thing."

For six months Gertrude lectured all over the country. From the East Coast she traveled west, then south, and back north again. Alice was always close at hand, manipulating circumstances and people so Gertrude's life would be as comfortable as possible. Gertrude loved the attention lavished on her, so much so that she postponed returning to France.

Then one morning while drinking a late coffee in bed she read an editorial from the Hearst press. "Is Gertrude Stein not Gertrude Stein," the author asked, "but somebody else living and talking in the same body?" Gertrude put the paper down. Such a question shook her very roots. Here it was again, the question of her identity. Why should someone who didn't know her ask such a question? And why did it frighten her so?

Gertrude shivered and lay back against the pillows. She closed her eyes and slipped back in time until she was a child of ten looking at the stars and asking herself, "How can I be living in finite space when I can see the stars in infinite space? What do I have to do with time and space?" At the time she had been a small girl under the great heavens, feeling no sense of personal identity at all. Always before she had been Gertrude Stein and she had known it—but at that moment who was she? Terrified, she had run sobbing into the house.

"Alice!" Gertrude called, abruptly bringing herself back to the present.

"Yes?"

"Come here, please."

"What is it?"

"I wish to leave for France," Gertrude said, wadding the editorial into a ball. "We have had enough of America. Make arrangements as quickly as you can. We are going home to the quiet of Belignin. I need to think, and I need to find an identity that I lost when I was ten years old."

Back in France Gertrude threw herself into a frenzy of work. She *would* come to terms with herself. "I am I," she wrote, "because my little dog knows me." But no, that wouldn't do. That said nothing about her self-identity, it spoke only for the dog's recognition.

An ethereal voice began to haunt her: "My name is Meg and the world is round. My name is Meg and the world is round." Gertrude searched her brain. Where had she heard that before? Then she remembered a cold dreary day in London and a haggish woman cackling, "Ain't she cute when she's drunk?" In her mind Gertrude saw Meg's thin white arms and heard her sing with angel clarity. How could this child have been so sure of her identity and her place in the universe? Living in squalor and poverty, her song had still been convincing. But then Gertrude had been convinced, too, before she was ten . . . perhaps if she wrote a children's book . . . yes! She had been wanting to write one anyway for a friend's child, Rose d'Aiguy.

Gertrude began a story and named it *The World is Round.* In it she told of a little girl, Rose, who wondered if she would still be Rose if her name were not Rose. With a blue garden chair in hand, she climbed a mountain in search of herself and to prove her courage, but when she arrived at the very top and was really all there and was not afraid anymore—*then* what was she to do? When Gertrude arrived at this point, she was baffled. Well, what *was* Rose to do? She was to marry Willy and live happily ever after, Gertrude quickly concluded. Writing children's stories was obviously not going to lead her any nearer to her own identity.

Gertrude's thoughts now turned to the one aspect of her character that she was certain of—her genius. She began to write *The Geographical History of America or the Relation of Human Nature to the Human Mind.* In this work she examined the identity of genius. Genius, she decided, was genius only if it could stand above human emotions. Sorrow, joy, love, fear—all these were indicative of a lower consciousness. This was not to say that a genius couldn't experience emotions, but only that he was able to transcend them into higher concepts. He possessed a level of consciousness that was purely narrative. And writing, Gertrude declared more firmly than ever, should be "a simple narrative of what is happening."

With this idea fresh in her mind, Gertrude abandoned for the time being her search for herself and wrote *Everybody's Autobiography*, a simple narrative and a sequel to *The Autobiography of Alice B. Toklas*, in which she related events that happened in America. Random House was quick to accept the manuscript when she offered it to them for publication.

Rumors of war were again sweeping across Europe. "It cannot happen a second time," Gertrude told everyone confidently, "There has been one world war, there cannot be another." In spite of daily evidence to the contrary, Gertrude clung to her convictions.

Alice, however, felt differently. "I think we should move to America as Michael and Sarah have done," she said. "We may not be as fortunate in another war as we were in the last one."

"Have Michael and Sarah moved to America?"

"Didn't you read the note they sent?"

"No. Not that it matters. They can do as they please. *We* are staying in France. There isn't going to be another war!"

In 1936 Gertrude was again invited to lecture at Oxford and Cambridge. This time she accepted without hesitation and lectured with no recurrence of stage fright. Her long exposure to the public in America had reduced her fears to their proper proportions.

When she and Alice returned to Paris, the threat of war loomed larger. Still Gertrude closed her mind to such a possibility. "You are an ostrich bird," Picasso told her. "You refuse to see the ugly truth."

But Gertrude would not be baited into an argument. She had more imminent issues than war to argue with Picasso—he had begun to write poetry. He even thought it was good. One night she went to his apartment and listened to him read:

At 4 in the afternoon
not at 5 the
lightning-swift arrival of
the merry-go-round
's daughter
fixes the colors in the tureen
the light grows
indifferent and
suddenly
it went sour the
dance with the merry-go-
uncle

After listening for some time, Gertrude began to feel relieved. Had Picasso's poetry been good, she would have been angry. But since it was so bad, she only felt "funny," as if a trusted friend were stealing something—and right in front of her nose. It bothered her, this thing about Pablo writing poetry. She left without commenting.

Several months later Picasso cornered her. "Did you like my poetry?" he asked.

"No, it was not poetry. You cannot write poetry."

"You are wrong, Gertrude. I *can* write poetry."

"Listen, Pablo," Gertrude said, grabbing him by the lapels. "You know very well you can't. Go on with it if you want, but don't be an ass and call it poetry."

"Well," Picasso said, shaking himself free, "supposing I do know that I can't write poetry—what then?"

"Then," Gertrude said sweetly, kissing him on both cheeks, "you will paint a beautiful picture and then more beautiful pictures and you will never try to write poetry again."

With the question of Picasso's poetic ability settled, Gertrude turned to capitalizing on her fame. Picasso was marketable, so she wrote a long loquacious essay on him. She was marketable, so she wrote a piece called *Paris, France*, and featured herself. When both these manuscripts were immediately accepted by publishers, Gertrude was annoyed. Suddenly she didn't like her work to sell so easily; it gave her nothing to fight against. Henry James' words came back to her, "An artist's theme is interesting only so long as an artist remains a failure. As long as he is a failure, he remains a person, but when he succeeds, he disappears into his work and there is no person left." Fame! How could she live with it?

Gertrude's melancholy was unexpectedly interrupted by the voice of their landlord at 27 Rue de Fleurus. "You must move," he said. "You must move at once."

"But how can we?" Gertrude protested. "We have made this address historical."

The landlord shook his head. "That is no concern to me. My son is moving in, and you are moving out."

"Well," Gertrude sighed, "I guess we have made 27 Rue de Fleurus so historical that it cannot hold us any longer."

Friends, hearing of Gertrude's and Alice's misfortune, told them of a vacant apartment over a bookbinder's establishment at 5 Rue Christine. The two women went to see it.

"Yes, this will do very nicely," Gertrude said almost at once.

"This apartment is too small," Alice protested. "You are taking it only because you dislike the inconvenience of looking further."

"Nevertheless," Gertrude maintained stubbornly, "this one will do nicely."

Alice viewed the living quarters with dismay. "How will we ever get our furniture, our paintings, our books, our knickknacks, and us into such a small apartment?"

Gertrude didn't answer. As usual, she was certain Alice could manage, somehow. And Alice did. Within days their furniture and belongings had been moved up the outside staircase that led to the apartment, and 5 Rue Christine had taken on a comfortable homey look. The rooms were "stuffed," but Gertrude liked them that way.

"We will be happy here," she assured Alice.

Alice was too tired from the ordeal of moving to argue. "Yes, Gertrude," she said wearily, "we will be happy here."

twenty

"What is the answer, Alice?"

With Gertrude's and Alice's change of address from 27 Rue de Fleurus to 5 Rue Christine, one crisis seemed to follow another. They had hardly settled in their new quarters when their dog Basket became very ill and died. Gertrude was devastated. She wanted to go out at once and get another poodle as nearly like Basket as possible.

"Do not do it," Picasso advised. "If I died, I wouldn't want you to find another Picasso just like me."

Gertrude paid no heed. She left the apartment, and when she returned, she was leading a white poodle. "We will call it Basket II," she said simply.

That summer, 1939, Gertrude and Alice made their yearly move to Belignin, but their spirits were low, for there was no doubt—very soon war would be declared. The two women were visiting friends near their home when the undeniable news arrived. "They shouldn't!" Gertrude cried, jumping up from her chair, her face white with fear. "Oh they shouldn't!" Later, when she and Alice were walking home and Gertrude had had time to think past her immediate alarm, she said, "There is this something about war, though. If there has to be one, I would rather be in it than out of it."

The two friends hurried back to Paris on a thirty-six hour pass to get their belongings and to pack their paintings. Even though D. H. Kahnweiler, an art dealer friend, tried to help them, they soon discovered that little could be done to protect art treasures from the ravages of war. The best they could do was place the paintings flat on the floor and hope there wouldn't be bombings nearby.

Nor was it safe to travel with such valuable canvases. Confusion reigned throughout France, and there was always the danger they would be stopped and robbed. "You shouldn't take any of them," Kahnweiler said. "But if you must, choose two—no more!" Gertrude and Alice chose their favorite Cézanne and also Picasso's portrait of Gertrude. The rest they left, and quickly returned to Belignin.

Although the booming of cannon could be heard all around them, Gertrude and Alice were not too uncomfortable in their country home. They had bread and honey and fish to eat and vegetables in abundance from the garden. Fuel, too, was plentiful. Alice kept busy by making Gertrude as comfortable as possible. Gertrude stilled her fears by reading detective and adventure stories and taking long walks with Basket II.

In 1940, when Italy entered the war, Gertrude was terribly frightened. "We are in everyone's path," she told Alice. "I think we should leave for Spain." Alice thought so, too, and they began to pack. They were almost ready to leave when Gertrude went to say goodbye to her friend, Dr. Chaboux. "Where are you going?" he inquired.

"To Spain. Belignin is no place for two American Jewish women with the Germans advancing so rapidly."

The doctor looked thoughtful. Then he said, "I would advise you to stay. Everyone knows you here, everyone likes you. We will help you in every way. Don't risk yourselves among strangers."

"Dr. Chaboux is wise," Gertrude told Alice when she returned home. "We will follow his advice and stay. But we must be ready for anything. Only the affection of our neighbors can save us."

Gertrude's faith in their neighbors was well placed. When the Germans called for a list of all the inhabitants of the area, the names of Gertrude Stein and Alice Toklas were deliberately omitted. The officials of Belignin did this at great personal risk. Had the Gestapo suspected such a conspiracy, those officials involved would have faced certain imprisonment, perhaps even death.

The biggest inconvenience Gertrude suffered from the war was lack of freedom. She liked to be in control of what happened in her life. In war there was only one area she could manipulate with certainty—writing. She turned to it with singular concentration.

By the fall of 1940 she was deeply involved in a novel, *Ida*, again exploring her favorite subject, identity. The following year she worked on *Mrs. Reynolds*. Here she told of an ordinary couple living an unexciting life who rose above the commonplace because they did not experience personal suffering from anything that happened. Through this novel Gertrude projected a deep-felt wish that her life with Alice could be simple, ordinary, and free from the horrors of war, both real and imagined.

The two friends were just getting used to their new and rigorous life when in 1942 they were once more asked to move from a place they loved, this time from their country home in Belignin. Gertrude was so upset that she took the case to court—quietly, so the Germans wouldn't know about it. The judge ruled against her, but allowed her an extension of time to find another house.

They found a lovely home situated against the mountains and surrounded by parks of bushes and trees. Since it was only twelve miles from Belignin, moving wasn't difficult. But even though their new home was modern and had many advantages over the old one, both Gertrude and Alice were heartbroken about leaving. Furthermore, they were afraid they wouldn't enjoy the same protection they had in Belignin.

One afternoon soon after they moved, a message came directly from the free government of France. "You must flee this area and go to Switzerland," it warned. "If you don't there is little we can do to save you from being taken to a concentration camp."

"What shall we do?" Alice exclaimed, thoroughly alarmed.

Gertrude put the message aside. "We will stay," she said firmly. "To leave we would have to falsify our passes. That we cannot do. Wherever we go, we will go regularly, even to a concentration camp."

Having successfully met one crisis after another, Gertrude felt strong enough to write about the war itself. She began putting down her thoughts and observations. "I will end my book," she promised, "when I see the first American soldier."

On August 31, 1944, while shopping in Belley, she was told there were American soldiers at the hotel. "Lead me to them," she cried. When she arrived at the hotel, there they were. "God bless you!" she shouted. "Oh God bless you indeed." And she hugged them and they hugged her and everyone congratulated everyone. Finally, after Gertrude had kissed them all, she went home and ended her book about war.

Germany surrendered on May 7, 1945. The French peasants were wild with joy. "No sober faces in the villages after *this* world war," Gertrude said as she and Alice walked through crowds of singing, dancing people.

"Does that mean there's not going to be another war?"

"I hope so," Gertrude answered, shouting to be heard above the ever-increasing din of cheers and songs and clapping. "Oh I certainly do hope so!"

Gertrude and Alice stayed in the country until mid-December, then they went back to Paris. Although friends had written saying that their possessions were still intact, they were fearful that it couldn't be true.

When they arrived at their Rue Christine apartment, the official stamp of the Gestapo was on the door. Cold horror ran through Gertrude as she thought of the terrors she and Alice had so fully escaped. But inside the apartment, very few things had been disturbed. Miraculously the rooms looked much as they had when the doors had been hurriedly locked five years before.

Adjusting from the harsh restrictions of war to the lively excitement of Paris was a welcomed change for the two women. Friends gave parties for them, and once again Gertrude was sought after as a celebrity. Invitations to speak came in the mail almost every day; one of them came from the United States Government asking her to make an official tour of bases in occupied Germany.

She responded good-naturedly to these requests and gladly talked to the streams of G.I.s who sought her out as one of the main attractions of Paris. A certain tiredness began growing in her, but she dismissed it and kept doing all she could to please the soldiers. When Alice protested, Gertrude silenced her by saying, "I shall never forget how the American soldiers liberated us. If they want to see me, I will be here. After all, they were there when we wanted to see them."

In spite of excessive demands on her time, Gertrude kept to a writing schedule. By early March, 1946, she had completed a book about American G.I.s, *Brewsie and Willie*, and also a libretto for a new opera to be done with Virgil Thomson. Based on the life of the suffragist Susan B. Anthony, she called it *The Mother Of Us All.*

One afternoon near the middle of July, a young would-be writer sought her advice on rewriting. "Do *not* re-write," Gertrude told him. "Either the phrase must come or it must not be written at all. If you have something to say, the words will be there. If the story does not come as a whole, it has been spoiled. That is the most difficult thing in writing, to be true to yourself, and to know yourself enough so that there is no obstacle to the story's coming through complete." Suddenly she stopped. Dark spots danced in front of her eyes, and she felt very weak.

The young man, sensing something was critically wrong, excused himself and left.

Alice was frightened. "Please," she begged, "let me call a doctor."

"No, no," Gertrude protested gently. "I am only tired. In a few days I will have my strength back, and we will take a vacation. Then I will rest."

Within a week Gertrude had bought a new car and was ready to go on the trip she had promised Alice. Picasso, seeing her driving a new car, demanded, "Why did you buy such a kind as this?"

"Because I like the way it looks. Why are you so disgruntled?"

"It isn't the kind I wanted for you."

"Pablo," Gertrude said, patting him on the hand, "I have never, since knowing you, done what you wanted for me. There is no need to start now."

"Yes, that is so," Picasso acknowledged, and walked away.

Gertrude's spirits were high the morning they started on their trip. She loved summer, especially when she could drive through the countryside. She chatted gaily as they drove along. Alice, however, was quiet.

"Why are you so solemn?" Gertrude inquired.

"Oh Gertrude, I'm worried about you. That last spell . . ."

Gertrude threw back her head and laughed. "You are a silly goose to bother your head about nonsense. What is there to worry about? I'm seventy-two; I have a few pains and sometimes I get a little tired. Now what is there to that?"

Alice looked out the window and didn't answer.

Gertrude laughed again but this time not so loudly. Dark spots were once more dancing in front of her eyes, and she was feeling ill—very, very ill. Before long she had to stop the car. Unmistakably something was wrong.

With the help of a passing motorist, Alice rushed Gertrude to Azay-le-Rideau. There a doctor visited her in an inn where they found quarters. "You are seriously ill, Miss Stein," the doctor said soberly. "I suggest you leave at once for Paris, where a specialist can oversee your case."

Alice engaged the services of a nurse, but Gertrude refused to be cared for. When it was time to board the train for their trip to the American Hospital at Neuilly-sur-

Seine on the outskirts of Paris, Gertrude was more interested in looking at the French landscape than in arriving in Paris on schedule. She hurried from one side of the train to the other, intent on missing nothing.

"Come along, Gertrude," Alice urged, "the train will not wait."

"No, no, not yet. I haven't seen it all!"

"You must come now," Alice gently insisted.

Reluctantly Gertrude gave in and allowed the nurse to take her aboard. When the train stopped, an ambulance was waiting to take Gertrude to the hospital. There a series of tests were conducted, and then she was allowed to sleep. When Gertrude awoke, two doctors were standing over her. "Well," she said, clearing her throat, "you look serious. What have you discovered about me?"

The senior doctor answered. "We have examined you, Miss Stein," he said, "and find that you are suffering from an advanced stage of malignant cancer."

Gertrude looked at him sharply. "Then why aren't you preparing me for an operation?"

"Because I have advised against it."

Gertrude stared at the doctor for a long time and then glanced at Alice, who was sitting in a chair near the bed. Her eyes were full of tears. Gertrude turned back to the doctor. "I *will* have an operation," she said firmly. "And as soon as possible."

The operation was scheduled for the afternoon of July 27. As Gertrude lay in bed waiting for Alice, her thoughts, naturally enough, turned to the mysterious problem of death. Much as she disliked the idea, she supposed that if she must die there was little she could do about it. Her life had been long and full. By hard work and courage she had achieved a real measure of success. Only one thing bothered her—she still hadn't solved the question of her identity.

Suddenly an idea occurred to her. Was she unable to find the answer because she didn't really know the question? The night before her father died, he had said, "carefully define the problem. Once the problem is properly defined, the answer is relatively easy." She couldn't define the problem of identity because every day she changed and thus one day's solution would not do for another. Now she understood what she had first noticed in the paintings of Cézanne: life and true art express a diffused center, not a climactic one, and always it extends beyond the frame.

She looked up to see Alice standing by the bed. Gertrude took her hand. "What is the answer, Alice?" she asked.

Tears streamed down Alice's face. "I don't know, Lovey."

The hospital attendants came in and put Gertrude on a cot. They rolled her toward the operating room. Alice walked along beside her, murmuring words of affection and comfort. At the door Gertrude stopped them. With great effort she pulled herself up to a sitting position. Her eyes twinkling, she kissed Alice on the cheek. "Here is a riddle," she whispered. "If you don't know the answer, then what is the question?" Chuckling softly, she lay back down.

The attendants waited for her to settle herself comfortably, then precisely, efficiently, they pushed Gertrude Stein through the doors.

A Selected Bibliography of Books by Gertrude Stein

Stein, Gertrude, *The Autobiography of Alice B. Toklas*, New York, Harcourt Brace and Co., 1933.

——, *Before the Flowers of Friendship Faded, Friendship Faded*, Paris, Plain Edition, 1931.

——, *Brewsie and Willie*, New York, Random House, 1946.

——, *Everybody's Autobiography*, New York, Random House, 1947.

——, *Four in America*, New Haven, Yale University Press, 1947.

——, *The Geographical History of America*, New York, Random House, 1936.

——, *Geography and Plays*, New York, Haskell House, 1967.

——, *How to Write*, Paris, Plain Edition, 1931.

——, *Ida*, New York, Random House, 1941.

——, *Last Operas and Plays*, New York, Rinehart and Company, Inc., 1949.

——, *Lectures in America*, New York, Random House, 1935.
——, *Lucy Church Amiably*, New York, Something Else Press, 1969.
——, *The Making of Americans*, New York, Harcourt Brace and Co., 1934.
——, *Mrs. Reynolds*, New Haven, Yale University Press, 1952.
——, *Paris, France*, New York, Charles Scribner's Sons, 1940.
——, *Picasso*, New York, Charles Scribner's Sons, 1939.
——, *Portraits and Prayers*, New York, Random House, 1934.
——, *Tender Buttons*, New York, Claire Marie, 1914.
——, *Things as They Are*, Pawlet, Vt., Banyan Press, 1950.
——, *Three Lives*, New York, The Grafton Press, 1910.
——, *Useful Knowledge*, New York, Payson and Clarke, Ltd., 1928.
——, *Wars I Have Seen*, New York, Random House, 1945.
——, *The World Is Round*, New York, W.R. Scott, 1939.

A Selected Bibliography of Books About Gertrude Stein

Bridgman, Richard, *Gertrude Stein in Pieces*, New York, Oxford University Press, 1970.

Brinnin, John Malcolm, *The Third Rose: Gertrude Stein and Her World*, Boston, Little, Brown, 1959.

Gallup, Donald Clifford, ed., *The Flowers of Friendship: Letters Written to Gertrude Stein*, New York, Alfred A. Knopf, Inc., 1953.

Miller, Rosalind S., *Gertrude Stein: Form and Intelligibility*, New York, Exposition Press, 1949.

Reid, Benjamin Lawrence, *Art by Subtraction*, Norman, Okla., University of Oklahoma Press, 1958.

Rogers, W. G., *When This You See Remember Me: Gertrude Stein in Person*, New York, Rinehart and Company, Inc., 1948.

Sprigge, Elizabeth, *Gertrude Stein: Her Life and Work*, London, H. Hamilton, 1957.

Stein, Leo, *Appreciation: Painting, Poetry, and Prose*, New York, Crown Publishers, 1947.

Stewart, Allegra, *Gertrude Stein and the Present*, Cambridge, Harvard University Press, 1967.
Sutherland, Donald, *Gertrude Stein: A Biography of Her Work*, New Haven, Yale University Press, 1951.
Toklas, Alice B., *What is Remembered*, New York, Holt, Rinehart and Winston, 1963.
Van Vechten, Carl, ed., *Selected Writings of Gertrude Stein*, New York, Random House, 1934.

Index